THE WOMAN WHO COMMANDED FIVE HUNDRED MILLION MEN

THE
WOMAN WHO
COMMANDED
500,000,000
MEN

BY CHARLES PETTIT

TRANSLATED FROM THE FRENCH BY
UNA, LADY TROUBRIDGE

HORACE LIVERIGHT : NEW YORK

PART ONE
YE-HO-NO-LA
Imperial Concubine

THE WOMAN
WHO COMMANDED FIVE
HUNDRED MILLION MEN

CHAPTER ONE

At the end of the reign of the illustrious emperor
Tao-Kouang, Holy Man and Son of Heaven as were
also his predecessors, there lived in an ancient house
in the Street of Pewter in Peking, on the threshold
of the Forbidden City, a Manchu family of high
lineage, but very moderate resources.

The father, who had commanded one of the Eight
Manchu Banners, had died prematurely, leaving to
his inconsolable widow an inheritance mainly con-
sisting of noble traditions and the care of three
young children.

The eldest of these was a little girl of remarkable
intelligence and quite astounding beauty. She was
called Ye-Ho-No-La, thus bearing the actual name
of the celebrated clan, to which her family belonged,
and on which she was later to confer such signal
honour, when she had become the all-powerful
Empress Tseu-Hi.

From her earliest childhood, Ye-Ho-No-La had
received an aristocratic education and a training

The Woman Who Commanded

designed to enable her honourably to take her place in exclusive society. At ten years of age, she had already the presence of one born to reign, and was able, under the cloak of the most refined courtesy, to impose her wishes upon her playmates. . . .

One of these, by name Yong-Lou, was a boy of her own age, who was destined by her influence to become a celebrated marshal and one of the most notable men of the Celestial Empire.

Nor was Yong-Lou her inferior in noble Manchu extraction. Of handsome appearance, blessed with perfect health and dowered with superior intelligence, this young aristocrat seemed fated to adorn the phenomenal career of Ye-Ho-No-La. It was a fact that even before the birth of the two children, a not unusual project of family alliance had coupled their names. Yong-Lou therefore entered the world as the predestined bridegroom of Ye-Ho-No-La.

Moreover, the two children early developed so strong a mutual affection that the choice of their hearts came all unknowingly to ratify the secret schemes of their parents. Entirely subjugated by the charms of his small companion, Yong-Lou overwhelmed her with tenderness and thoughtful care; thus all unconsciously courting the favour of her who was to become arbitress of his entire career.

At that period it must be admitted that he might easily have adopted the dominant rôle, since he was already promoted to those robes which in the East are associated with virility, while Ye-Ho-No-La wore in all humbleness the trousers reserved for the weaker sex.

But Yong-Lou instinctively discerned in Ye-Ho-No-La an exceptional individual, while he could hardly be expected to foresee that in an immense empire where women were utterly despised, his young goddess would rise to an eminence from which she would cause five hundred million men to cower beneath her terrible dominion.

For the time being, he was content to play knuckle-bones with his wonderful little playmate, being courteously careful to allow her a supremacy that might awaken less innocent ambitions.

It must not be supposed that either of these model children would have conceived it possible publicly to infringe the laws of etiquette.

They would greet one another ceremoniously, observing all the traditional rules of the most elaborate courtesy; the words they used were elegant and precious as though they already played their parts before an entire universe. Only their ardent eyes exchanged a thousand confidences, and these confidences were eagerly welcomed by their precocious minds.

It was perhaps hardly surprising that a moment arrived when the mother of Ye-Ho-No-La thought it wise to put an end to these silent but eloquent avowals.

The Woman Who Commanded

In any case, Ye-Ho-No-La, having attained the age of puberty, was constrained by immutable custom to enter upon an existence of industrious retirement in the women's apartments, where she would be moulded into an accomplished young woman.

Yong-Lou viewed the enforced separation with profound melancholy, but he could only resign himself to the wisdom of the ancient law.

Five Hundred Million Men

CHAPTER TWO

In the seclusion of the schoolroom of the dismal women's apartments, Ye-Ho-No-La lent a respectful ear to her venerable mother, who read aloud in sententious accents a passage from the Sia-hio, a remarkable little moral treatise composed many centuries earlier by the ancient Tchou-Hi, who flourished under the Song dynasty.

"As regards females," declared that excellent lady, "so soon as they shall have attained the age of ten years, they shall no longer be permitted to leave the house. Their teacher will instruct them in the art of temperate and gentle speech, and in that of a constantly serene and affable demeanour; above all things she will instil the necessity of obedience; she will also teach them to weave, to wind silk, to spin, to sew and to fashion all feminine apparel. In the ancestral cult, they shall pour the wine and serve the meats and vegetables; they shall invariably maintain a modest and decent aspect and their reverence for the rites shall suffer no intermission."

At this juncture, Ye-Ho-No-La, while remaining with her head bowed in deference to the edifying precepts enunciated by her venerable mother, instinctively allowed her thoughts to stray.

The Woman Who Commanded

Before her respectfully lowered eyelids floated the vision of those happy hours of childhood when she had been free to enjoy the sunshine and the open air. Clearest of all appeared the image of Yong-Lou. She now knew with certainty that her enchanting young playmate, who had so early conquered her childish heart, was in due course destined to become her husband. It was true that many melancholy hours must elapse before the happy day. Even when the project of marriage should be publicly ratified, she would still have to endure the delay occasioned by the innumerable ritual formalities, the succession of visits and interviews between the members of the two families and finally the astrologers must be consulted and persuaded to fix an auspicious day for the celebration of the ceremony. But the ultimate end of all these trials would be unalloyed bliss. Of that she had no doubt, and her conviction gave her the strength to smile inwardly at the prospect of a rosy future.

Meanwhile, the matron, setting aside the ancient Tchou-Hi's famous treatise, was dilating in learned terms upon the three duties of dependence and the four cardinal virtues imposed upon a good wife by the secular laws of seemliness. And Ye-Ho-No-La, who was now listening with more attention, reflected upon the future day when the society of her beloved husband would relegate all such pompous twaddle to complete oblivion. She none the less appreciated

her mother's motives in inculcating principles worthy
of her high social position, and she inwardly determined always to maintain outwardly a proud and
hypocritical appearance of consideration for the
fundamental and traditional virtues. She was therefore happy to instruct herself in all those rules of
politeness and in that knowledge of the world necessary to a great lady of exalted rank in the Empire.
It was unfortunate that such rules should be so
numerous and so complicated! In spite of the wisdom with which Confucius had included them in his
immortal masterpiece, there remained the necessity
of also studying every commentary added thereto by
all the principal scholars of China.

Ye-Ho-No-La spent entire days laboriously deciphering these documents, though she was already
cognisant of over ten thousand ideograms; a remarkable achievement in a very young girl.

She also made use of her constantly increasing
erudition, in the study of the four holy books, which
are an indispensable adjunct to a genuinely classical
education, and she displayed a prodigious interest in
Chinese history, as though she already knew by
intuition that she was herself destined to act upon
its stage.

Finally, as an additional outlet for her superabundant energies, she took an enthusiastic interest
in all the arts, while specially attracted towards
poetry and painting. Brush in hand, she would

delicately seek to describe in noble characters the landscape that she had drawn upon the spotless rice-paper.

Had she felt herself completely immune from her mother's watchful eye, it is certain that her chosen theme would have been love, and that her eager fingers would have sought to immortalise the beloved features of Yong-Lou.

Five Hundred Million Men

CHAPTER THREE

Ye-Ho-No-La was fifteen years old. The moment approached for the consummation of her projected union with Yong-Lou. Already the two families were exchanging visits, compliments and trifling gifts; there was talk of consulting a celebrated astrologer as to the propitious month and day for the celebration, when the most terrible of all catastrophes plunged the Celestial Empire into a strictly compulsory mourning of twenty-seven months' duration. In other words, the Holy Man, Tao-Kouang, Son of Heaven and Lord of Ten Thousand Years, chose this inconvenient moment for his ascent of the Dragon's Chariot. When a species of god disappears in this manner, it naturally behooves the entire universe to remain shrouded in darkness, while no sound but that of wails and lamentations must be heard.

It should be clearly understood, of course, that never for an instant does the Dragon's Throne remain unoccupied: such a contingency would be as death to a people to whom their ruler, the Son of Heaven, is both a temporal and a spiritual father. The heir-presumptive, Hien-Foung, had therefore immediately succeeded his father Tao-Kouang as Holy Man, but he himself was constrained to remain officially prostrated by his immense sorrow throughout the prescribed twenty-seven months. It followed as a natural consequence that all the families in the Empire, more particularly those of the conquering Manchu race, must remain in a like state of affliction, at any rate in so far as concerned all outward manifestations.

It was therefore not the moment for the celebration of the feasts connected with the marriage of Yong-Lou and Ye-Ho-No-La. An astrologer could scarcely have been found to discern an auspicious day in so mournful an epoch. The merest hint of such a thing would have jeopardised his reputation and very possibly his head into the bargain! Ye-Ho-No-La was thus constrained further to enhance her marvellous education in the seclusion of the women's apartments. She was, moreover, profoundly moved by the universal mourning that so particularly affected her race and her clan, for it must be recognised that the future Empress was instinctively and incessantly concerned with the greatness of the Celestial Empire. Her patriotism was a violent and irresistible passion which invariably governed her and survived every other emotion.

Even in extreme youth she nourished that exacerbated and almost savage patriotism which she retained to her dying hour, and which led her alike to perform the finest actions and to commit the most celebrated crimes of her life. In the vanished Holy

Man, she very sincerely mourned a remarkable ruler and a member of her own clan who thus became the foremost of those ancestors to whom she was always to offer a filial and sacred veneration.

She loyally donned, as did her mother, her brother and her sister, the appropriate white mourning garments, and retired into seclusion as though she had herself been widowed. She did not, of course, cease to think of Yong-Lou, but instinct and pride of race now led her to concentrate her deepest emotions upon the newly enthroned Son of Heaven. Of what nature was this Holy Man, who personified in her eyes not only the glory of the conquering dynasty, but the actual prosperity of herself and of all those belonging to her? She vaguely knew that although not yet twenty years of age, he already mourned one legitimate spouse. What other woman would be chosen to take her place? Who would be elected the favourite among the numerous concubines who would throng the harem so soon as the official mourning should end? Here was food for much reflection on the part of a young girl who could not fail to realise that by virtue of the high rank of her family, she might easily be summoned to take her place as an Imperial Concubine in the Forbidden City.

The Woman Who Commanded

CHAPTER FOUR

The great day arrived when the twenty-seven months of the Imperial mourning having come to a close, Ye-Ho-No-La was summoned officially to the Violet Town, to be presented to the Dowager Empress, who was desirous of selecting from among the young daughters of the Manchu aristocracy, thirty concubines for the use of her divine son, the Holy Man, Hien-Foung; it may be added that her desire was in complete accordance with the most reputable traditions.

Ye-Ho-No-La, as the daughter of a general who had commanded one of the Eight Manchu Banners, could fittingly aspire to the honour of entering the harem of the Lord of Ten Thousand Years.

It was however essential that she should find favour in the eyes of the venerable Dowager Empress, since that lady not unnaturally required that her divine son's concubines should also be her humble servants; a requirement that was equally in accordance with the best traditions.

It was thus of primary importance to Ye-Ho-No-La that she should not fail to please the ancient lady who was to become her second mother, in the sense that she was to be the future object of respect, obedi-

ence and unqualified submission. It was therefore
fortunate that Ye-Ho-No-La had been from her
earliest childhood accustomed to perform with un-
impeachable correctness all those genuflexions and
prostrations exacted by ritual from a young girl in
the presence of distinguished company.

Her excellent mother had in this respect afforded
her the best of all possible trainings in consistently
requiring from her daughter the most complicated
salutations and in severely reprimanding the smallest
deficiency. Moreover, Ye-Ho-No-La possessed in all
her person such innate distinction that she was able
to perform the most complicated ritual with supremely natural grace and truly aristocratic elegance.

She was therefore immune from all fear of nerv-
ousness or awkwardness in attending a Court ceremony, but such confidence by no means guaranteed
an entry into the good graces of an aged lady! It
was, in fact, not merely a question of escaping cen-
sure, but of attracting some measure of her approval.

Undoubtedly her primary aim must be to maintain
a submissive and respectful attitude in accordance
with the laws of etiquette; but the effect must be
achieved while completely avoiding any appearance
of lifeless stupidity such as might suggest a lack of
humour and intelligence. And then in the matter of
words, what subtleties must be observed, what difficulties surmounted!

Reflecting upon the terrible ordeal that awaited

The Woman Who Commanded

her, and which was to determine her entire destiny, Ye-Ho-No-La experienced a profound emotion. Her excellent mother, while fertile in sage recommendations, was scarcely less perturbed. The entire future of the family did in point of fact depend upon this one cast of the dice, not to speak of its prestige in the eyes of other families! That Ye-Ho-No-La should be summoned to the Violet Town as a candidate for imperial concubinage was in itself a high mark of the esteem accorded to her parents; but should she fail in the trial, how deep would be the disappointment, not to say the shame of her relations! In these circumstances the image of Yong-Lou receded into a dim past that seemed already distant.

For the moment Ye-Ho-No-La gave herself into the skilful hands of the tirers, manicurists and hairdressers who crowded around her. She was clad in a long tunic of rose-coloured silk which fell below her knees, but was open at the sides in order to display her mauve trousers. The panels of the tunic were embellished with marvellous embroidery. Her feet were swathed in skilfully disposed bandages of the whitest linen and her coloured silk slippers were enhanced by high felt heels which added dignity to the young girl's carriage. Her headdress, in accordance with Manchu custom, was monumental. Ye-Ho-No-La's long black tresses were piled upon the crown of her head in a gigantic diadem secured by large gold pins. Although of medium stature,

20

Five Hundred Million Men

Ye-Ho-No-La, thanks to her towering headdress, her high heels and her long tunic, appeared unusually tall, an effect which harmonised with her long flexible throat and flowing sleeves.

As for her complexion, it was nothing short of a masterpiece, worthy of a master hand. The tints were skilfully blended from the deep rose of her cheeks to the pure white of her neck; delicate greenish shadows enhanced the crimson of her lips; her eyebrows were accentuated in the form of a V above her almond-shaped eyes which sparkled between heavily shaded lids. Her hair, oiled and perfumed, shone blue-black like a raven's wing and was further adorned by splendid ornaments of silver, blue enamel and pearls.

Ye-Ho-No-La smiled her self-satisfaction into the brass mirror which gave back the flash of her white teeth.

She was really an extremely lovely person, worthy to arouse the appreciation of the Holy Man, the Son of Heaven.

The Woman Who Commanded

CHAPTER FIVE

Prior to entering the litter which was to convey her to the Dowager Empress' palace, Ye-Ho-No-La made a final prostration before the tablets of her ancestors, imploring the assistance of their spirits; then she flung herself at the feet of her venerable mother in order to receive, with all due respect, that lady's valedictory counsels.

Finally she quitted with deep emotion the parental abode, while her sister and brother waved a last farewell. Huddled in the obscurity of her litter, concealed by closed shutters from any intrusive glances, she had leisure to reflect with some anxiety upon her astonishing adventure.

The bearers advanced at a rapid pace, crying: "Hé! Han! Hé! Han!" while the herald-at-arms, who preceded them, shouted himself hoarse in his efforts to obtain free passage.

Eunuchs from the Palace, accompanied by Manchu soldiers, trotted alongside, escorting the future Concubine of the Holy Man. The weather was warm and overcast; at intervals the procession encountered caravans of camels which raised clouds of malodorous dust, and also strings of blue-hooded carts on large yellow wheels, drawn by well-kept mules. It passed eminent mandarins, military officers perched like monkeys on their Tartar horses and civilians dozing in the penumbra of their azure-coloured palanquins.

Among the crowd of pedestrians who were roughly jostled aside to make way for these Excellencies, wandered shaggy-haired dogs and long-legged black swine. Men and beasts alike sweated in perfect harmony.

Attentive to the spectacle of the public streets that she so rarely beheld, Ye-Ho-No-La was none the less careful constantly to raise to her delicate nostrils a phial of attar of roses, as became a young aristocrat who could not with propriety permit herself to be suffocated by the stench of the populace. On the very threshold of one of the gates which afforded access to the Forbidden City, Ye-Ho-No-La received a painful shock. Within a few paces of her palanquin she beheld Yong-Lou, with a grave and sorrowful countenance, standing in the forefront of the idlers who had assembled to watch the flower of Manchu aristocracy vanish into the mystery of the Imperial Palace. The unfortunate young man could not distinguish behind the drawn blinds of the litter the features of her who was to have been his adored spouse, but he doubtless hoped that she would behold him and thus receive a final proof of his constant devotion.

At this last and most sorrowful appearance of her betrothed, Ye-Ho-No-La's virgin heart felt as though

it must break asunder. Past memories arose in a
flood to overwhelm her, together with all the ardent
desires of her amorous temperament.

But already the litter was entering the Violet
Town: Ye-Ho-No-La had vanished as though by en-
chantment; such is too often the conclusion of a
young girl's dreams,

Five Hundred Million Men

CHAPTER SIX

Very humbly Ye-Ho-No-La accomplished nine
genuflexions and as many prostrations before Her
Majesty the Empress Mother, who, seated upon a
throne upholstered in yellow brocade, appeared to
pay but scant attention to a chit of a girl who was
performing no more than the customary ritual.

Moreover, Her Majesty had to review over a hundred candidates, which could hardly fail to be a
tedious task. Having received with a noble indifference the respectful homage of this youthful flock, She
ordered them to parade before Her in single file with
a view to judging of their dignity and grace, addressing to each in turn a few words which required a
brief reply. At the conclusion of this examination
She commanded the withdrawal of those who struck
Her as plain or unintelligent, then, addressing the
remainder, She informed them that they were to have
the immense honour of entering the Imperial Harem.

Taking into consideration the recent examen and
also the family rank and recommendations of the
candidates, She then proceeded to allot them their
titles. Following an established custom, the women
of the Holy Man were divided into four categories:
the "fei," the "pin," the "kouei jen" and the "tchang

tsaï." Among the present candidates, none was elected "fei," for a concubine only deserves such an honour after she has given evidence of merit. One candidate, specially favoured as being the sister of the late young Empress, was at once elected "pin," and the Empress Mother informed her that she would replace her deceased sister as Empress Consort to the widowed and childless Son of Heaven. As for Ye-Ho-No-La, she had the comparative good fortune of being one of those chosen to be "kouei jen," that is to say, "honourable persons," which was by no means a bad beginning.

She might easily have had to content herself with the rank of "tchang tsaï," or she might even have been sent about her business.

It was therefore with genuine gratitude that she threw herself once more at Her Majesty's feet in so graceful a manner that the old lady was secretly gratified. Ye-Ho-No-La thus achieved the first step in her career; it had become vitally important, above all other considerations, to capture the favour of the Dowager Empress, who by tradition possessed absolute dominion over all the women in the Forbidden City, from the Empress Consort down to the humblest slave.

Ye-Ho-No-La was then conducted with much ceremony by the attendant eunuchs to her new abode.

This proved to be a delightful pavilion, with curved gables adorned by little silver bells; it was moreover a prison from which she must never again emerge under any pretext whatsoever, short of being summoned to spend a night of incredible felicity in the chamber of the Son of Heaven.

The Woman Who Commanded

CHAPTER SEVEN

It was a great honour to have obtained the title of "kouei jen"; all ambitions were now legitimate for the new "honourable person." But many dreary hours must elapse before the divine night when she would at length be admitted to the Chamber of the Sacred Repose.

Such enforced seclusion, such an empty, sterile existence must inevitably dismay a warm-blooded young virgin. Her problem was to find a means of occupying her mind and of employing her physical energies in this dismal solitude.

The first moment of triumph was followed by realisation: Ye-Ho-No-La must resign herself henceforth to being no better than a humble slave in the harem. She belonged, body and soul, to the Imperial Household!

All greatness has its servitude, and a thousand regrets assailed the recluse, especially when she reflected that that very hour might have found her in the arms of an idolised husband, scaling all the heights of happy emotion and partaking of all the pleasures of love.

At seventeen years old, it is very hard to behold the gates of love closing before one's eyes for ever.

Five Hundred Million Men

To Ye-Ho-No-La there undeniably remained the glorious hope of one night sharing the couch of the Son of Heaven; but it requires almost a religious vocation gladly to sacrifice earthly love on the altar of a mysterious spiritual devotion! Ye-Ho-No-La was as yet doubtful of this vocation. Her restless thoughts persisted in evoking with some bitterness the bliss that she had renounced; the image of Yong-Lou arose incessantly in a fevered brain that should have been exclusively illumined by mystical visions of the Son of Heaven.

As she sat immersed in sombre reflections, seeking somewhat unsuccessfully to repress her exacerbated senses, she was surprised to see the door of her chamber pushed ajar, disclosing the smiling countenance of a young man of unusual and delicate beauty.

The heart of Ye-Ho-No-La leaped within her breast: could it be the Son of Heaven Himself, come in defiance of all precedent to visit his poor little "honourable person"? What a strange adventure, and how worthy to be graven upon the tablets of History!

But already the mysterious individual had entered the room with a certain familiarity, and although he had greeted Ye-Ho-No-La with perfect regard to the canons of the strictest etiquette he did not seem afraid to stare persistently at her in a manner that was by no means as seemly. Somewhat abashed, Ye-Ho-No-La lowered her lids with becoming modesty. She thought the young man charming, but extremely indiscreet.

Whereupon he addressed her in a voice of curious quality:

"Young lady, you have every appearance of being worthy of the title that has been conferred upon you by Her Majesty the Empress Mother! Your countenance has celestial loveliness, your eyebrows are arched like those of a dragon, your eyes shine like stars on the brow of night, and your teeth glisten like the drops of dew which sparkle at the dawning of a spring day. . . . As for your hands, the very least that I can say of them is that one could believe them to be carved out of the purest jade."

Having cleared his throat as though seeking to shake off some embarrassment, this astounding young man concluded with delightful simplicity:

"It now remains for me to examine the unseen portions of your divine person. . . . Will you therefore, young lady, be so kind as to remove all your clothing?"

Ye-Ho-No-La, who had not expected such a peroration, could not refrain from exclaiming with regrettable impulsiveness:

"And pray, sir, what are you, that you should venture to make such a suggestion?"

At these words the young man smiled faintly:

"What am I? . . . Have you not remarked that the Hour of the Cock draws to a close; the sun sets;

twilight descends on the Violet Town like a mysterious shroud. . . ."

Ye-Ho-No-La offered no reply, failing to apprehend his meaning.

He resumed:

"What am I? . . . At this hour no male is permitted to remain within the forbidden precincts excepting only the Holy Man. . . . Did you not know it?"

Much moved, she exclaimed:

"I am his most humble servant!"

He lightly shrugged his shoulders:

"And I, Madam, am the yet humbler slave of the Son of Heaven, being permitted to remain at his service, even, and indeed particularly, during the hours of darkness. . . . What am I? . . . You must by now surely have understood. . . ."

And suddenly there was daylight in the mind of Ye-Ho-No-La.

In spite of herself, she murmured between her teeth:

"How very unfortunate . . . and such a delightful young man!"

But already he had resumed.

"The favour of her Majesty the Empress Mother has deigned to place me in command of the castrates who watch day and night over the Forbidden City; I am the Grand Eunuch Ngan-Te-Hai "

At the sound of the renowned name which she had

so often heard her mother pronounce, Ye-Ho-No-La hastened to perform the various salutations due to so august a court official. She also began humbly to excuse herself for having failed to render him immediate homage.

He interrupted her with a gesture:

"I am not displeased with you . . . you appear to be a charming young woman, if a trifle inexperienced. . . . But now that you know who I am, pray do not delay any longer with your unrobing . . . custom and ritual demand that I should assure myself of your intact virginity and your perfect state of health. . . . Bear in mind, young lady, the fact that you will one day be summoned to the chamber of the Holy Man! . . . Need I say more?"

Five Hundred Million Men

CHAPTER EIGHT

In obedience to the orders of the Grand Eunuch,
Ye-Ho-No-La had removed all her garments and now
awaited a detailed examination by Ngan-Te-Hai. In
spite of herself she was overwhelmed with confusion.
When one has grown up a model little girl, deeply
respectful to convention, and who would rather have
died than risk the exposure of so much as an ankle
even to the chosen suitor, it is particularly embarrass-
ing to find oneself stark naked alone with a strange
young man.

Of course, it was not really a man who approached
her, and she sought to gain confidence by assuring
herself that the performance was quite without sig-
nificance. None the less she remained confused and
rather perturbed.

Ngan-Te-Hai's behaviour was most unusual. He
appeared as profoundly moved as though he had still
retained all his virility; his features were drawn, his
eyes shone with a strange radiance and his hands
were shaken by a convulsive tremor.

Ye-Ho-No-La could not avert her eyes from those
singular and remarkably beautiful hands. They
seemed at once to allure her and to give forth extraordinary magnetic currents.

In order to escape from this obsession, she closed

her eyelids, but her heart beat as though it must break in her bosom.

It now appeared that Ngan-Te-Hai employed curious methods in the accomplishment of his official duties. An impulse of revolt possessed Ye-Ho-No-La, but she reflected that it would hardly be policy on her part to repulse with severity the person upon whom depended all her career. Mastering herself, she endeavoured to retain her physical equanimity.

The examination, however, was prolonged almost beyond human endurance. Ye-Ho-No-La, yielding at length to nervous excitation and opening her eyes, beheld a spectacle at once touching and absurd; she beheld a tear coursing slowly down the cheek of Ngan-Te-Hai. Feeling himself observed he regained his self-control, and ceasing his caresses, calmly announced:

"Young lady, I have the honour to inform you that the report which I have to make concerning you to Her Majesty the Empress Mother is in all respects favourable. You are definitely adjudged worthy to share the august couch of the Son of Heaven."

Whereupon he uttered a heart-rending sigh.

She inquired with some anxiety:

"Have I perhaps unknowingly caused you pain?"

He made no reply, but stood gazing at her with a kind of ecstasy. Then, passing his hand across his brow as though to banish an evil dream, he turned upon his heel and left her without a word.

CHAPTER NINE

Before a moon had passed, Ye-Ho-No-La had at any rate succeeded in completely winning the heart of the Grand Eunuch, who, since the death of the Emperor Tao-Kouang, had become all-powerful in the Forbidden City. Hien-Foung, the new Son of Heaven, in no respect resembled his illustrious father; a young man devoid of energy and of small intelligence, he quickly permitted the Empress Mother to establish the reign of women and of eunuchs. The energetic and warlike Manchu nobles beheld with deep anxiety the brilliant Tsin dynasty tottering to its decline, and China, lacking a real leader, gradually sinking into lamentable decay.

But what could they do? The Son of Heaven, like a God in His Tabernacle, remained inaccessibly buried in the Violet Town, and none but the Dowager Empress and the Grand Eunuch could aspire to approach or influence him.

Monarchy by right divine can be the greatness of a nation, provided the monarch himself be of superior calibre, as in the case of the earlier emperors of the Tsin dynasty, and notably in that of the super-genius Kang-Yi; but when absolute autocracy falls into the hands of a degenerate, it spells disaster and ruin.

The Woman Who Commanded

Ye-Ho-No-La was as yet ignorant of this decline; she retained the atavistic cult of the Son of Heaven and her ambitions centered upon becoming his bride of a single night. Meanwhile, she had gained the entire confidence of the high priest of her mysterious deity, which was quite undeniably a brilliant achievement.

Ngan-Te-Hai now spent nearly all his leisure hours with the concubine of whom he had made, without admitting it to himself, something in the nature of a mistress. It was a strange attachment that arose between this castrate and the young virgin, in which a love denied fulfilment found expression in the flower of fruitless caresses, and where only their spirits could truly unite in a fantastic ecstasy. From the very first day, Ngan-Te-Hai had attempted no concealment. He had openly proclaimed his despair at thus belatedly discovering his incarnate ideal when he could no longer love her as a man.

As an old man might do who had outlived his virility, he beheld the adored idol of his youthful dreams, she of whom he had vainly evoked the image when in possession of all his powers, had at length appeared, but too late; she could now awaken only vain and cruel regrets.

Ngan-Te-Hai had narrated to her with disconcerting candour the entire story of his life, telling her of his childhood in the little town of Ho-Kian-Fen, an educational district that boasted the peculiar glory of having furnished the most celebrated eunuchs to the Court of Peking. Of an altogether seductive appearance, gifted with superior intelligence and innate distinction, he had been singled out by prominent castrates who had urged him to enter their powerful confraternity. For a long time he had hesitated; warm-blooded and of ardent temperament, he adored women to excess; then came the pressure of financial difficulties. He and his family had been ruined. His filial piety, so strong a sentiment in China, would not allow him to leave his old parents without means of subsistence, or expose them to the shame of lacking handsome coffins. Therefore, with despair in his heart, and after having duly and respectably secured himself a posterity that would render him the obligatory ancestral honours, this excellent father and citizen, this devoted son, had resigned himself to the supreme sacrifice.

He narrated in full detail the cruel operation to Ye-Ho-No-La, who listened in horror. In pathetic accents he evoked the scene; the doctors, in pointed caps similar to those worn by executioners, courteously inquiring as was customary: "Are you a willing patient?" And when in trembling accents he had faltered the fatal affirmative, the stunning blow on the point of the jaw that served in lieu of an anaesthetic. Followed the terrible agony as of dissolution. Finally came elaborate treatment, and several days of torture during which he had hung between life and death . . . did not great numbers succumb to the operation!

Thanks, however, to his robust constitution, he had survived, and having received all the congratulations of the surgeons, astonished at their failure to kill him, he had duly entered upon the Career! From that moment immediate and phenomenal success had attended him. Entering as an official in the household of Prince Tchouen, younger brother of the Holy Man, Hien-Foung, he was so successful in attracting the favourable attention of the Dowager Empress, that she quickly transferred him to the service of the Son of Heaven. In an incredibly short time he was advanced to the all-important office of Grand Eunuch, thus becoming the confidential favourite of their Majesties, and acquiring a redoubtable power before which the noblest in the land were constrained to bow in submission.

But Ngan-Te-Hai could only gaze sadly at the exquisite concubine and conclude his autobiographical recital with a gloomy shake of the head.

Whereupon Ye-Ho-No-La would wonder whether to laugh or weep, since the love she had aroused in this notable eunuch was a thing both absurd and pathetic.

Five Hundred Million Men

CHAPTER TEN

Twenty moons had elapsed since the entry of Ye-Ho-No-La into the Imperial Harem, and the youthful "honourable person" was still vainly awaiting a summons from the Holy Man.

She was distressed and humiliated at this apparent disdain.

Life seemed to her an empty and mournful affair. When one is the daughter of an illustrious warrior and a conqueror's blood boils in one's veins, when one is capable of every ardour and of all the passions, what an inane outcome of ambitious dreams to find oneself vegetating uselessly in the most banal of seclusions!

To be a neglected slave when one aspires to dominate a universe is a cruel dispensation of providence!

One day, unable any longer to contain herself, Ye-Ho-No-La confided her bitterness to Ngan-Te-Hai, who alone could in some measure attract the attention of the Son of Heaven to his concubine.

She was surprised to find that at her very first words Ngan-Te-Hai appeared as disturbed as any lover whose mistress should threaten him with betrayal.

The Woman Who Commanded

The impotent being had conceived the insensate dream of retaining exclusive possession of the loveliest woman in China, and he experienced a strange spasm of jealousy which wrung his heart.

He suffered severely at the mere thought that this exquisite creature should belong to another than himself, and that other a real man who would initiate this adored virgin in the pleasures of real love. By means of a crude act of which he was himself incapable, his rival, achieving an easy conquest, would lamentably profane the ideal of his soul.

To be absolute lord of a chosen beloved, and one moreover reserved for a god's embraces, here was fit revenge for the castrate who suffered under masculine contempt and derision! And now he was being asked to renounce the supreme delight of being the strange and only lover of his heart's ideal!

In a trembling voice, Ngan-Te-Hai faltered:

"Can you not be contented as you are? . . . No trouble or anxiety can disturb the even tenor of your days. . . . You have but to express a desire and I shall seek to gratify it! . . . No matter what your caprice may be . . . you will always find me at your command!"

To all of which Ye-Ho-No-La replied rather dryly:

"Undeniably you are the best and most devoted of friends, but I cannot resign myself to leading a life as useless as it is retired. . . . Something tells me insistently that I have another part to play. . . . To me it seems that a voice from Heaven commands me and that the spirits of my Ancestors adjure me to take action for the glory of the Celestial Empire and for the honour of my race. . . ."

She paused, breathless. The emotion which overcame her was sincere and splendid. With tears in his eyes Ngan-Te-Hai had fought for composure. He also was now thinking of the future.

She quickly and passionately resumed:

"Yes, let me be perfectly honest . . . you, Ngan-Te-Hai, will remain lord of my affections; but let that content you, and do not ask for more!"

Seeing that he remained doubtful, she exclaimed:

"Be satisfied with what I can give you, and if you truly love me be proud to see me attain to a position worthy of you and of myself. . . . The Son of Heaven is childless, as you have often told me. . . . Well! Learn that I, a humble concubine of tertiary rank, have conceived in my heart the formidable project of giving birth to an heir to the Throne. . . . Yes, I admit it frankly. . . . I desire to take a place in History! . . . I am only a woman, but I am determined that my renown shall equal that of my most glorious ancestors. . . . I have the audacity to inform you that I nourish every ambition and that nothing appears to me impossible because I feel myself irresistibly urged by occult forces toward universal dominion. . . ."

The Woman Who Commanded

Ngan-Te-Hai contemplated with stupefaction this extraordinary concubine who stood before him as proudly and as impressively as though she were already Empress Mother. He instinctively foresaw that she was fated to rise to the height of her ambitions and was no mere visionary.

Having reflected deeply, he at length replied:

"You are perhaps in the right . . . and I am prepared to sacrifice myself. . . . I will do my best to ensure that the jade tablet bearing your name shall be the one to fall beneath the Hand of His Majesty the Holy Man when next he deigns to share his couch with one of his concubines. . . . It must however be confessed that His Majesty is unfortunately little inclined towards women. . . . The Empress Consort herself endures the most distressing neglect and I am not even prepared to affirm that she does not still retain a very humiliating virginity. . . ."

Ye-Ho-No-La could not refrain from inquisitive inquiry:

"Is it possible that the Holy Man is inaccessible to earthly enjoyments?"

Ngan-Te-Hai repressed a sarcastic smile:

"Out of respect for the Throne, I must refuse to enlighten you further . . . but allow me to advise you, if you aspire to advancement, not to overlook the high favour in which you have always been held by the Empress Mother. . . . She, and she alone, can still exert over her divine son an influence which may

recall him to the exercise of his privileges. . . ."
Ye-Ho-No-La would gladly have asked further ques-
tions, but at this point the eunuch relapsed into
uncommunicative prudence.

The Woman Who Commanded

CHAPTER ELEVEN

On the very next day, the Empress Mother, privately incited thereto by the Grand Eunuch, deigned to fly into a terrible rage with her divine son the Holy Man, Hien-Foung.

She reproached him bitterly with being nothing but a debauched and drunken degenerate, and with sacrificing the future of the dynasty to his shameless pursuits.

"Not only," she concluded, "do you completely neglect the affairs of the Celestial Empire, which you leave to the care of your younger brother, Prince Kuong, but you are incapable of begetting an heir to the Throne or even of engendering an ordinary bastard, and this in spite of the fact that you have at your disposal the Empress Consort and several dozen concubines, each one more enchanting than the last. . . ."

"Euh! Euh!" interposed the Holy Man, between two drunken hiccups. "Permit me, most venerable Mother, entirely to disagree with you."

"What do you find wrong with them? Are they not irreproachably submissive both to you and to the rites? . . ."

"Undoubtedly! . . . But how conventional! . . .

44

What utter brainlessness! . . . I am so infernally bored in their society that I now prefer to avoid the very sight of them, although I am quite ready to admit that they are ornamental."

"It is not a question of always looking for amusement," exclaimed the Empress Mother. "It has become necessary to show your People that you are not a castrate . . . all your predecessors have gloriously affirmed their virility . . . you are the first to cover the Throne with ridicule. . . . I, your own mother, am ready to die of shame!"

The poor lady might have spared herself the trouble of trying to sting the Holy Man to even a semblance of self-respect. He remained completely insensible to her valuable and maternal advice.

She jibed:

"Your minions have so entirely swamped your personality that you can no longer perceive anything else in the world. . . . Your cousins most especially, the Princes Tsaï-Youen and Touan-Houa, seem to strike you as delightful."

"They are infinitely less idiotic than my women, which is something to the good; they at least know how to amuse me at all times. . . ."

"And in what a manner! Every moon the Grand Censor reports to me, bitterly lamenting your lack of dignity."

"The Grand Censor bores me," replied the Holy Man calmly. "I shall order him to be beheaded."

The Woman Who Commanded

Then the Empress Mother proffered her ultimatum:

"Since you answer me in such a manner, I also will assert my authority. . . . As your mother I command you to abandon your minions and accomplish your virile duty . . . and if you do not obey me, I shall proclaim throughout the Celestial Empire the fact that you have failed in filial respect . . . and that is a disgrace from which even you will not recover, for all your cynical apathy. . . . Everything in the world is permitted to you, excepting the neglect of your filial duty. . . . In that respect, even the Holy Man must bow to divine law, like the humblest of his subjects."

Having spoken, she raised her arms as though calling heaven to witness the unworthiness of her ignoble offspring.

Then Hien-Foung, in spite of himself, experienced a profound perturbation. His mother was right; he was capable of the vilest imaginable conduct, but he dared not in the face of History officially sin against filial piety! Bowing his head, he murmured:

"Venerable Mother, it shall never be said that I have offended against you . . . I will obey!"

Whereupon the Empress Mother at length consented to moderate her angry tone of voice:

"I congratulate you," she remarked, "for having retained that shred of self-respect which forbids you to outrage me by persisting in your shameless refusal to give an heir to the Dragon's Throne. . . . You can rest assured that if I appear harsh, I am acting not only for your personal good, but also for the honour of your dynasty and for that of the Celestial Empire! . . ."

With these words she majestically withdrew.

Hardly, however, had she reached her palace, than she sent hurriedly for the Grand Eunuch in order to issue her commands.

The chastening of the Holy Man might well be transitory and it was urgent to draw profit from it while it lasted.

The Woman Who Commanded

CHAPTER TWELVE

That night a red lantern was lighted before the pavilion occupied by Ye-Ho-No-La, for the Holy Man had nonchalantly handed to the Grand Eunuch the green jade tablet upon which were inscribed the titles of that particular "honourable person."

Ngan-Te-Hai was overwhelmed. The ineffably cruel moment had actually arrived when he himself must deliver over to the gross desires of a male, the ideal creature whom a strange illusion had led him to regard in some sort as a dream mistress.

He suffered unendurably, if not with his senses, at any rate with his heart and his mind. Ye-Ho-No-La, out of compassion, restrained her joyful pride and sought to console him:

"Who knows," she declared, "if I may not have the supreme good fortune of being fructified by the act of the Holy Man! . . . And in that case, Ngan-Te-Hai, only think how immense will be your personal power! . . . For I swear to you by everything that I hold most sacred, that I shall always remain the most faithful of friends!"

But the castrate would only shake his head sadly.

"The fairest of dreams must have an end! . . ." he sighed. Then he announced:

Five Hundred Million Men

"I can only bow before the Imperial Will. . . . Be so good as to follow me, young lady. . . . The hour has come! . . . The sun goes to rest. . . . The Son of Heaven, in accordance with the rites, must do likewise. . . . At this moment he enters the Chamber of the Sacred Repose . . . where you must not longer delay to join him."

"Reverence to this!" replied Ye-Ho-No-La, in the ceremonial tradition that accorded with so solemn an occasion.

They soon found themselves in the Great Red Vestibule which led to the Chamber of the Son of Heaven. A cohort of eunuchs with bared swords gravely kept watch before the door. Impassive and mute, their aspect struck terror to the heart. A weighty and majestic silence reigned in the immense hall.

From the dimly illumined walls glowed the gilded ideographs of austere and sententious maxims; the heavy tables of crimson lacquer loomed like slumbering monsters, the dragons with which they were decorated opened threatening maws, and the grey flags of the pavement were splashed here and there as with blood by reflections from the big red lamps of oiled paper suspended from the huge ceiling beams. The general effect was as mysterious as a temple. One divined the proximity of some species of God, enclosed in his shrine. Never had Ye-Ho-No-La experienced so profound an emotion.

49

The Woman Who Commanded

At this solemn moment when she was about to find herself in the presence of the Son of Heaven, she felt almost annihilated by the grandeur of the part which she was to play.

Her legs trembled beneath her so that Ngan-Te-Hai was forced to support her; a mystical faith possessed her; she thought only of the redoubtable event which was to make her the bride of a god. When the Grand Eunuch, having performed all the customary ceremonies, half opened the door of the Chamber of the Sacred Repose, she almost swooned away.

Not daring even to look before her, her head bowed and her eyelids lowered, she took a few faltering steps and, trembling from head to foot, flung herself prostrate, striking her forehead on the ground, a desperate suppliant. Already Ngan-Te-Hai had withdrawn on silent feet; the heavy doors were closing slowly. She was alone, entirely alone in the presence of the Holy Man. . . .

Five Hundred Million Men

CHAPTER THIRTEEN

Ye-Ho-No-La never knew how long she remained thus prostrate. Lost to consciousness in a species of ecstasy, she was no longer aware of her surroundings. Her brain was without thought as her body was without strength; only her heart beat as though it must break from her bosom, causing her an anguish that was her one remaining link with the outside world.

At length, however, she began to recover a measure of consciousness, but only in order to endure a new anguish of anxiety.

She began to reflect:

Had the Holy Man so much as perceived her presence? . . . Would he in compassion condescend to speak the word which would at least enable her to emerge vith decency from a position which threatened to be eternal! . . . What should she do? . . . She could neither move nor speak without encouragement from the Son of Heaven; to do so would be against every tradition! . . .

The moments passed, moments so precious for her and upon which hung her entire destiny. . . . Soon would come the hour when, according to custom, the Holy Man would leave his Chamber in order to preside at the matinal and daily meeting of the Grand

Council, and it would then be too late to attract his attention. Poor little "honourable person"! She felt so small a thing before the crushing contempt of this god whom her soul so ardently adored! Truly her suspense was too cruelly prolonged!

Unable any longer to contain herself, Ye-Ho-No-La finally raised her head ever so slightly; then, gaining a little courage, she opened her eyes. . . . She promptly experienced a severe mental shock, having at length beheld the Son of Heaven! . . . Alas for her disillusionment! . . . She suddenly felt as though she were in a nightmare. . . . Could this indeed be the Son of Heaven, this blotchy, drink-sodden young man, sprawling ungracefully upon a state bed, to all appearances completely overcome by his alcoholic excesses!

The deep and enduring faith of Ye-Ho-No-La vanished as she beheld the spectacle of this lamentable deity; she became an atheist, a complete atheist, at any rate in so far as concerned His Majesty. Once more in entire control of her faculties, she regained her judgment, together with a cold and lucid energy. Before her eyes, in place of a god, she beheld the caricature of a man; the event was at once dolorous and fraught with possibilities!

Obviously the ecstatic raptures she had dreamed of must give place to physical disgust, but what a tempting prey was this degenerate who must be devoid of personality, of will-power, and even of dignity.

Five Hundred Million Men

She coldly surveyed the imperial marionette who might so soon be her plaything if only she had the audacity to grasp the strings. For the moment, the Son of Heaven was staring with a glassy eye at the bottles of liqueur and of rice spirit which were arranged upon a little table at his bedside.

Moreover these bottles were his only preoccupation! No other thought had entered his mind. In the absence of his minions, who had been removed by the energetic action of the Empress Mother, he had sought consolation in the indulgence of his secondary vice: he had relapsed into imperially drunken torpor!

That the loveliest woman in China should have remained for more than an hour prostrate at his feet, vainly expecting that he should condescend to remark her, was a fact that left him completely unmoved! . . . As Son of Heaven he could permit himself any demeanour with respect to women and was free to regard them if he chose as non-existent! . . . His mother was the solitary exception to this rule, but it was no good feeling that dictated his filial submission . . . he was merely afraid of offending against the sacred law, the only authority which he dared not defy.

Meanwhile Ye-Ho-No-La, summoning up her growing confidence, gradually assumed an erect position and very quietly approached the bed. To do so was flatly opposed to tradition, but she had now determined to strike for success, if need be even at the peril of her life, and to risk everything upon a single throw of the dice.

At that very moment the Son of Heaven slightly turned his head and at length caught sight of the concubine standing beside him in utter defiance of the most elementary etiquette.

He made a faint gesture of surprise; already Ye-Ho-No-La felt her courage ebbing and was about to prostrate herself once more, when His Majesty checked her by a magnanimous movement. . . . After all, what did he care about lapses of etiquette! . . . She struck him as tolerably attractive and as less foolish than his other woman. He even condescended to say in a sodden voice:

"You are certainly quite as well got up as the other concubines, little as such details appeal to me. . . . But you really do appear to be relatively alive, so you may as well make yourself useful and pour me out a drink."

Ye-Ho-No-La gracefully hastened to fill a jade goblet with a potent rice spirit which stank at ten paces, but which, because of its potency, was particularly affected by the Holy Man. Then, throwing to the winds all ostentatious respect, and omitting the thousand and one customary rules of service, she promptly handed the goblet to her impatient lord.

Hien-Foung appeared genuinely grateful for this lack of respect toward his Illustrious Person, since it enabled him the sooner to slake his drunkard's thirst. Having emptied his cup in a single draught, he mumbled:

"You do undeniably seem much less idiotic than those insufferable dolls whom they generally thrust upon me. . . . If I could only make you understand the horror in which I hold the sacred rites, I should be glad enough to receive you more frequently than any other concubine in this deadly Chamber of the Sacred Repose to which tradition has doomed me."

Then Ye-Ho-No-La, encouraged by so promising a beginning, launched herself to the assault like a true warrior's daughter.

In an ingratiating voice she murmured:

"Since Your Majesty permits me to speak, I will venture to solicit a great favour . . ."

She paused, as though appalled at her own audacity, but she nevertheless hardily extended her hand towards one of the bottles.

The Son of Heaven smiled an ineffable smile.

"I understand . . . she actually has a taste for liquor . . . she can keep me company exactly like one of my dear minions. . . . Ah, young lady, if you could only know how much you delight me ! . . . What is your name? It seems to have already escaped me . . . although it was certainly inscribed on the jade tablet; but at that time it appeared so utterly unimportant. . . ."

Whereupon Ye-Ho-No-La promptly told him her name, and growing more and more audacious, she

began to converse, and even to laugh, while with
simulated eagerness she quaffed goblets of raw spirit
which cruelly burnt her very vitals; but where is the
sacrifice that cannot be accomplished by a clever
woman bent upon an imperial conquest?

The Son of Heaven placed an enthusiastic and
gallant arm round the waist of this "honourable person" who was enchanting him by her scandalous behaviour. Such a thing had never happened to him
before and he exulted; contrary to all expectations he
had at length found a boon companion in his vulgar
excesses. . . . Decidedly Ye-Ho-No-La was as good
as any minion! . . . She was as amusing, as vicious,
and, what was by no means to be despised, she was
also quite as good-looking.

Five Hundred Million Men

Amid general stupefaction, Ye-Ho-No-La had become the favourite of the Emperor Hien-Foung. This youthful "honourable person" had even acquired so great an influence over the feeble will of the Holy Man that he now refused to take any action whatsoever without previously asking her advice.

Every night she joined him in his chamber, to the vast confusion of all the other concubines who were now definitely disdained. The minions had disappeared and even the Princes Tsaï-Youen and Touan-Houa, the cherished cousins of the Emperor Hien-Foung, remained discreetly aloof.

Only the Empress Consort, out of respect for the rites, was still tolerated in the Chamber of the Sacred Repose, upon those nights indicated by the official astrologers when a conjunction of certain planets was propitious to an imperial union.

One fine day an amazing piece of news shook the Forbidden City like a clap of thunder: the "honourable person," Ye-Ho-No-La, had become pregnant by the act of the Holy Man!

An immediate official edict raised her from the rank of "kouei-jen" to that of "pin," the Empress Mother coming in person to confer her new title upon the concubine, accompanied by congratulations and expressions of the warmest gratitude. The Son of Heaven had at last affirmed his virility, the honour of the dynasty was saved.

From that moment the influence of Ye-Ho-No-La at Court continued to increase. She was no longer relegated to disdain and seclusion in a pavilion of the harem. The Grand Eunuch, Ngan-Te-Hai, was bribed with magnificent gifts by the most powerful personages in the land to convey to the favourite petitions which she was implored to present to the Son of Heaven. Meanwhile, Ye-Ho-No-La thought only of the child within her womb. Should she bear a son, her triumph would be assured!

Simultaneously the Empress Consort had also been declared pregnant.

She also was a prey to the self-same anxieties: should she be delivered of an heir to the Throne, she might hope to retain a supremacy over her rival the "pin" concubine, Ye-Ho-No-La, but what would be her position in the contrary event?

The important state officials prudently awaited results before joining either of the parties which had already been formed in anticipation of the future. Only incorrigible gamblers registered bets upon one side or the other. At this juncture, the Empress Mother abruptly ascended the Dragon's Chariot which bore her away to the Yellow Fountains. With her vanished the only temporal authority acknowledged by the Son of Heaven. Upon what woman would now devolve the supreme command of the Forbidden City during those long nocturnal hours when custom forbade access to the Palace to any male excepting the Holy Man? Undoubtedly Ye-Ho-No-La already effectively dominated the Violet Town: all the cohorts of eunuchs acknowledged her sway, while all the concubines and servants were her trembling slaves. But theoretically it was still the Empress Consort who alone reigned in company with the Holy Man. More perturbed than anyone was Ngan-Te-Hai, who by contributing to the rise of Ye-Ho-No-La had drawn upon himself the implacable resentment of the Empress Consort. Through this dangerous game he had risked his situation as Grand Eunuch, and possibly even the loss of his head.

And the third moon of the year was at hand, which should behold the dénouement of the drama.

A species of fever possessed the Court; people counted the days and the hours; information was eagerly sought regarding the merest tremor of the imperial wombs.

Finally, upon a beautiful spring morning, the Son of Heaven, entering the Chamber of the Grand Council, solemnly announced between two drunken hiccups that his favourite had made him father of a son, which son, bastard though he might be, was, failing legitimate progeny, heir presumptive to the Throne.

The Woman Who Commanded

"Reverence to this," murmured the high dignitaries, prostrating themselves, and the Princes Kuong and Tchouen, younger brothers of the Son of Heaven, swore allegiance to the newly-born.

The concubine Ye-Ho-No-La was promptly proclaimed "fei." No higher title could be accorded her, short of at once creating her Empress, and such a move was complicated by the existence of the Empress Consort who was also shortly to be confined, and by the fact that should she also produce a son, Ye-Ho-No-La's offspring would at once cease to be heir presumptive!

During more than a week there was general anxiety.

Ye-Ho-No-La tossed feverishly upon her bed. She continually summoned the Grand Eunuch in order to question him as to the latest developments.

When she learned that her rival was actually in labour, she could no longer endure her inactivity. She left her bed, although she was scarcely recovered from her confinement, and fell to supplicating heaven for a favourable issue: Let the Empress Consort be delivered of a dead child rather than of a son! Might she expire in labour! Who would care? And passionately Ye-Ho-No-La folded to her breast her own son . . . that son who was to be an Emperor or a nameless bastard.

After a cruel day of suspense, at the Hour of the Cock, she beheld for the hundredth time the Grand

60

Eunuch approaching her, but his face which had lately been clouded by anxiety was now wreathed in joyful smiles.

Ye-Ho-No-La cried eagerly:

"She has had a daughter!"

"Yes, Madam, only a daughter!" replied Ngan-Te-Hai in a voice of ecstasy.

Then Ye-Ho-No-La, for all her energy, felt herself swoon away with joy and pride.

The Woman Who Commanded

CHAPTER FIFTEEN

At this juncture the Emperor Hien-Foung, who
no longer had his mother to keep him to the narrow
path, and who, on the other hand, recked as little
of the warnings of the Tribunal of Rites as of the
criticisms of the Court of Censors, began once more
to indulge himself in the lowest debauches and the
most loathsome drunkenness. His excesses were such
that he soon had a kind of seizure which left him
half paralysed and completely stupefied. This event
greatly increased the power of Ye-Ho-No-La, for in
the opinion of the official doctors and even of those
humble outsiders who were permitted to approach
him, the Son of Heaven would in future be incapable
of begetting another heir. It was much to be thankful for that he could somehow be got onto his feet,
and could hobble, with the aid of crutches, as far as
the Chamber of the Grand Council, where, sprawled
upon his Throne, with haggard aspect and wander-
ing mind, he allowed his younger brother, Prince
Kuong, to direct the affairs of the Celestial Empire.

Ye-Ho-No-La, who, as mother of the heir presumptive, now ranked to some extent as a member of
the Imperial Family, had very skilfully slipped into

the good graces of Prince Kuong, who thought her both charming and of exceptional intelligence.

She soon exerted over this prince as complete a sway as that which she had acquired over the lamentable Hien-Foung; so much so that the prince began to seek her advice before deciding upon any enterprise. She moreover undertook to persuade His wretched Majesty, the Holy Man, to sign such decrees as they had jointly elaborated, he having retained in his helplessness an unalterable admiration for the mother of his only son.

Frequently it would be Ye-Ho-No-La herself who, taking advantage of the weakness of the Emperor Hien-Foung, would firmly append to the official documents the Seal of Supreme Authority without which no decree could become law.

Not content, however, with this share of power, Ye-Ho-No-La further reënforced the situation by marrying her sister to Prince Tchouen, second brother of the Emperor Hien-Foung; she then had no respite until her own brother was proclaimed Duke Tsaï with the entrée to the Court circle.

Naturally she did not forget her excellent mother to whom she owed her upbringing and much valuable advice.

She overwhelmed her with gifts and honours and caused it to be publicly announced that she would shortly pay her an official visit.

The Woman Who Commanded

CHAPTER SIXTEEN

By a special decree which she had obtained from the Son of Heaven, Ye-Ho-No-La was authorised to leave the Forbidden City for the purpose of visiting her mother.

This was an unheard-of concession and furnished sensational proof of the favourite's omnipotence, since she was thus permitted to transgress against every secular tradition. Never before had any concubine, even of "fei" rank, shown herself publicly outside the Harem; even the dowager empresses when called, during the minority of their descendants, to officiate at the meetings of the Grand Council, were concealed by a yellow silk veil from the ministers, who were only permitted to hear their voices.

And here was Ye-Ho-No-La allowed to issue forth from the ramparts of the Violet Town and to adventure all alone outside the sacred precincts! What an astounding act of independence! Surely the Manes of the ancient Imperial Censors must be turning in their graves!

At the dawn of the memorable day, Ye-Ho-No-La, with magnificent assurance, stepped into a palanquin upholstered in pale gold, the imperial colour, and giving the order for departure, proudly directed her

escort to the Street of Pewter in the very centre of
the Tartar Town.

The few pedestrians who encountered the cortège
could not believe their eyes; they prostrated themselves in stupefaction before this goddess who dared
to leave her tabernacle.

At the Hour of the Serpent, Ye-Ho-No-La reached
the maternal abode which she had not visited for over
four years!

She was shaken by profound emotion! A thousand
childhood memories arose in her mind, but they
seemed distant indeed! She found it hard to realise
that she had in so short a time climbed every rung
of the ladder of her ambition. Only yesterday she
had been the humble little virgin slave of rites and
traditions, the slave also of her family, and later of
the Imperial Harem; to-day she possessed the rank,
if not the title of Empress, and could dictate her
caprices to the vastest Empire of the Universe!
What a prodigious destiny!

In the meantime, she had alighted from her litter,
and leaving a cohort of eunuchs with drawn swords
on guard before the gates of the family domain, she
solemnly entered the inner courtyard where she had
so often in childhood played knucklebones with her
beloved playmate, Yong-Lou. At this thought her
heart endured a sharp pang; she had never forgotten
him who had been her betrothed and to whom in her
earliest youth she had given her affections. She

formed a sudden resolve to see him again at any cost, and to consummate the dream of her adolescence. . . .

The illustrious visitor was at once surrounded by a perfect salvo of rockets exploded in sign of proud welcome by the old family retainers. On the threshold of the house all her relations had gathered to render homage to her who had so glorified their clan, and out of respect for the mother of the future Son of Heaven, they met her with all the ritualistic genuflexions. The Sovereign passed proudly between two hedges of bowing relations to the Hall of Honour where she herself paid homage to the tablets of her ancestors, not excepting that of her father, the late Commander of the Eighth Manchu Banner. Then, overflowing with filial piety, she flung herself at the feet of that mother whom she had recently elevated to the rank of Duchess. All the beholders were moved to tears at seeing the "treasured spouse" of the Son of Heaven thus nobly fulfilling the dual duties of ancestral worship and filial obedience.

They were now not only dazzled by the splendour of her achievement, she had also made a conquest of their hearts.

For was not Ye-Ho-No-La, with the suavity of a great lady, bestowing graceful and friendly remarks upon all her relations and swearing to them with very evident sincerity that she would remain faithful to her race and that the Manchus should always preserve supremacy over every soul in China?

Five Hundred Million Men

And naturally, among the Manchus, those dear to her would be her first consideration. All the family could depend upon her favour. Could anything be better in the best of all possible worlds!

An ancient nonagenarian uncle very nearly succumbed to his joyful emotion! Everyone sat down to the feast. Ye-Ho-No-La had ceded the place of honour to her mother, but she felt no false modesty in occupying the second seat and in actually presiding at the banquet.

Throughout the afternoon she serenely received assurance of absolute devotion on the part of all her relations, accompanied by oaths of fidelity transmitted to her from the outer world by the absent members of her clan. As the Hour of the Cock drew near, Ye-Ho-No-La regretfully prepared to leave the family home so dear to her heart.

Before doing so, however, she wished to look once more upon the chamber where she had passed her adolescence of hard work, reflection and dreams. Adjacent to it, now empty and desolate, were the rooms that had once rung with the childish laughter of her sister and brother. It must be admitted that they for their part experienced scant regret at leaving the maternal roof, since one had left it in order to become the illustrious Princess Tchouen, sister-in-law of the Holy Man, while the other, the imposing Duke Tsaï, had the entrée to the Imperial Palace upon an equal footing with the leading mandarins. What an undreamt-of change for this predestined family!

Only Ye-Ho-No-La's worthy mother, despite her promotion to the rank of imperial duchess, continued to inhabit the house in the Street of Pewter to which she was attached by many precious memories and notably by the shrine of her ancestors.

Ye-Ho-No-La's desire was therefore powerless to attract her mother to Court, but before bidding her farewell, the concubine extracted from her the promise of frequent visits to the Imperial Palace, the doors of which would be always open to her in view of her newly-acquired rank.

Five Hundred Million Men

CHAPTER SEVENTEEN

The following moon, Yong-Lou, despite his extreme youth, was appointed to the command of the Manchu troops charged with the personal defence of the Violet Town and of the Throne: Ye-Ho-No-La had remembered the past!

She had moreover no difficulty in persuading Prince Kuong that it was necessary to their common security to place in command of the Manchu Guard a young and energetic man whose loyalty and devotion were above suspicion; it was essential to mistrust evicted courtiers, and notably the imperial Princes Tsaï-Youen and Touan-Houa, who were restive at their fall from favour. These first cousins of the Emperor Hien-Foung represented the clan of the minions, who had by no means abandoned all hope of returning to power.

On the other hand, the Empress Consort, while living a life of extreme seclusion ever since ill-fortune had cursed her with a daughter, nourished a secret rancour against her rival. She also had retained a certain number of adherents who might at any moment require repression.

Briefly, Yong-Lou was regarded by the clan of Ye-Ho-No-La as an indispensable protector who could be relied upon without hesitation in the gravest emergency. The young man, moreover, combined strength with charm; he was of unblemished courage and remarkable intelligence. As he was also of excellent birth and enjoyed immense popularity with the Manchu warriors, his advancement appeared perfectly natural, not only to Prince Kuong, but to all the ministers.

It was indeed necessary to have at hand some one of truly heroic nature who could be trusted from every standpoint, for the general situation throughout the Celestial Empire had been extremely unquiet since the incapable Hien-Foung had succeeded the illustrious Tao-Kouang. Rumours to the effect that the Son of Heaven was nothing but a hopeless degenerate had pervaded the Celestial Empire, and the five hundred million Chinese, who had always murmured under the Manchu yoke, were beginning to feel that the moment had come to abolish a decadent dynasty.

In every province, secret conspiracy was stirring; revolts were numerous, precursors of the coming revolution. Finally, in the very heart of China, a celebrated agitator, Hong, surnamed "the celestial king," announced that he had received a divine mission to overthrow the Dragon's Throne.

At the head of innumerable malcontents who had christened themselves the "Taï-Ping," this prophet had succeeded in gaining possession of Nanking, the

Five Hundred Million Men

Southern capital, and there, forming a State within a State, had for several years held in check all imperial troops sent to dislodge him.

Yong-Lou and his Manchu Guard therefore represented the final barrier in the event of the Taï-Ping, definitively victorious, daring to take the road to Northern China with a view to overthrowing the Tsin dynasty.

Moreover, not content with having served the interests both of her heart and of the Throne by the nomination of Yong-Lou to the command of the Guard, Ye-Ho-No-La, who was hourly becoming more active in public affairs, also insisted that General Cheng Kouo-Fang should immediately be sent against the Taï-Ping, he being the only military chief capable of such an undertaking, and one of the greatest heroes in China.

There again, Ye-Ho-No-La showed herself as energetic as she was eager in defence of the State. The members of the Grand Council vainly urged that General Cheng-Kouo-Fang having recently lost his parents, was by all decent traditions compelled to remain for twenty-seven months in mourning seclusion; the favourite insisted, proudly proclaiming that when the good of the Empire was at stake, the most sacred traditions must be overridden. She thus accomplished yet another act of authority: she dared to affront established ritual, a truly prodigious departure in the eyes of statesmen who were imbued with a routine that had the sacred sanction of several thousand years.

Deeply appreciating the courage displayed by Ye-Ho-No-La in this emergency, Prince Kuong fell permanently under the sway of this extraordinary creature who, in a land where women had never before played any prominent part, gave evidence of more than virile determination.

As it happened, General Cheng Kouo-Fang did not immediately succeed in crushing the formidable Taï-Ping insurrection, but he kept the enemy at bay and barred the road to Peking, which was at any rate a considerable advantage.

As for Yong-Lou, he at once acquitted himself marvellously of his duties, maintaining the most perfect order, not only in Peking but throughout Northern China, and thus enabling the dynasty to breathe freely while safely awaiting better times. In this manner did Ye-Ho-No-La, by means of her indomitable energy, postpone for half a century the period of terrible anarchy which has now overwhelmed the unfortunate Chinese nation among the ruins of the Dragon's Throne.

The most rabid revolutionaries were constrained to await the death of this superwoman before playing havoc with the established order, and even in these days, if they are superstitious, they must live in dread of her angry Spirit.

Five Hundred Million Men

CHAPTER EIGHTEEN

Having settled the affairs of the Celestial Empire and provisionally assured the foundations of the Dragon's Throne, Ye-Ho-No-La called to mind the fact that she was not only an all-powerful sovereign, but also the loveliest woman in China.

She was barely twenty-two years of age; her blood was as fire in her veins, and although she had already satisfied her mind by the realisation of limitless ambitions, she had been compelled to neglect every other enjoyment which life could offer.

She reflected bitterly that all she knew of love was that strange passion conceived for her by the Grand Eunuch, Ngan-Te-Hai, when first he had assumed control of her destiny. She bore him no grudge for that curious adventure: quite the contrary; now that their positions were reversed and he at her command, she retained for the singular dreamer all the affectionate compassion that a woman feels before frustrated love.

Ngan-Te-Hai had become her plaything, her dog, her favourite slave. She dominated him so entirely that he obeyed her lightest gesture and was ready, even at the risk of his life, to gratify her smallest caprice.

The Woman Who Commanded

It was in any case to their mutual interest to be able to trust each other implicitly.

When night fell, Ngan-Te-Hai became absolute master of the Violet Town, since he commanded the cohorts of eunuchs who mounted guard at all the palace gates and watched on the ramparts. It was therefore vital that he should be entirely devoted to Ye-Ho-No-La if she was to enjoy complete security while being free to do exactly as she pleased.

On the other hand, the Grand Eunuch's position was consolidated by the unswerving affection of Ye-Ho-No-La. Without it, the Empress Consort, his bitter enemy, as were Hien-Foung's cousins, the imperial princes, might well have obtained from Prince Kuong the downfall of Ngan-Te-Hai.

Ye-Ho-No-La and the Grand Eunuch were therefore allies in the Violet Town, at any rate during the hours of darkness.

In the daytime it was, on the contrary, Yong-Lou, the commander of the Manchu brigades, who was Ye-Ho-No-La's chief support. She had made his fortune, he owed her everything in the world, and he also would have allowed himself to be cut into small pieces sooner than he would have incurred her displeasure.

But Ye-Ho-No-La was not hard to please. She still felt for her former betrothed a passion which had only thriven upon opposition, and she eagerly awaited the propitious day when she would at length be free to realise the dream of her youth.

Five Hundred Million Men

At the time of her first entrance into the Forbidden City, she had for a moment almost renounced any conscious thought of the delightful emotion which had blossomed in her virgin heart; at that time she firmly believed that she was destined for the embraces of a god, and a kind of mystic love had dominated the love of the body.

But after the horrible disillusionment afforded by her first encounter with the Son of Heaven, the earthly love had resumed entire possession of her wounded heart. Ye-Ho-No-La now thought only of a means whereby she could create a favourable opportunity and give herself unreservedly to him whom she had loved since childhood.

If she was proud and energetic by nature, she did not by any means lack shrewdness, and suddenly, the springtime being at hand, she began to simulate a lively predilection for the Summer Palace, an imperial residence situated at about twenty lis' distance from Peking, beyond the northern ramparts of the Tartar town.

A canal, reserved for the use of the imperial family, connected the lake which lay before the Summer Palace with those of the Park in the Forbidden City.

At dawn, Ye-Ho-No-La would step into a magnificent barge hung with yellow silk, and would command the oarsmen to make all possible speed up the canal to the Summer Palace.

In order to "save her face" she would be accom-

panied by other sumptuous barges containing the Son
of Heaven Himself and the Empress Consort, together with a number of concubines, slaves and
eunuchs.

After them followed an innumerable army of servants, ranging from musicians to cooks, not to speak
of actors, in a word, all the people qualified to add
to the enjoyment of a summer residence where the
Court, far from political anxieties, was permitted by
long established custom to enjoy a period of pleasurable relaxation.

To protect the imperial procession on its way, the
banks of the canal were patrolled by faithful Manchu
warriors who galloped along on their little Tartar
horses, under the command of their valiant general,
Yong-Lou. With what joyful emotion did Ye-Ho-
No-La behold the pride and beauty of this gallant
horseman. What a contrast he presented to the
miserable Son of Heaven, extended, a mere remnant
of humanity, in the neighbouring barge! And yet this
degenerate had presumed to initiate her in the joys
of love. A cruel necessity had compelled her to act
a part, to receive his orders and to endure his clumsy
advances with a hypocritical smile upon her lips.
Vengeance would indeed be sweet!

It was only when she reached the lake before the
Summer Palace that Ye-Ho-No-La joyfully inhaled
the odour of freedom.

From that residence all useless conventions were

banished. Far from ministers and mandarins, equally far from public affairs and political intrigues, the imperial family was there happily at home, leading the simple existence of all-powerful landowners.

The Summer Palace, moreover, was of a fanciful beauty that enchanted all beholders. Gentle declivities were adorned by delicious pavilions whose intricate gables were further decorated by little silver bells that tinkled melodiously in the pure morning air. There were numerous terraces of which the white marble balustrades were mirrored in the blue waters of the lake, while the glazed tiles of the roofs caught and reflected a thousand rosy fires of dawn.

A vast white marble junk served as landing stage. The pale gold barges approached it in succession, greeted by the strains of flutes and violins. Their Majesties entered their ideal retreat.

Within the sumptuous rooms of the palace was a hoard of priceless treasures. On all sides were precious stones, gems and lacquer, cups of the purest jade and antique enamels, porcelains undreamed of by any collector in the world, bronzes fit to adorn any palace in the universe. It was incontestably the greatest art museum that has ever existed throughout the Far East.

Deeply artistic, a scholar of delicacy and erudition, Ye-Ho-No-La enjoyed to the full this accumulation of wonders in the Summer Palace. She spent long hours examining them rapturously, while the

Son of Heaven thought only of a quiet pavilion where
he might foregather with his bottles and his minions,
and the Empress Consort, melancholy and resigned,
sought another pavilion in which to conceal her boredom and her humiliation.

And that which was fated to occur was not long
delayed.

Ye-Ho-No-La, having ordered Ngan-Te-Hai to
establish the closest possible guard among the
eunuchs, to prevent any intruder from approaching
the pavilion wherein she sat composing elegant verses
and decorating delicious silk panels . . . Ye-Ho-
No-La none the less, upon a certain beautiful
afternoon, commanded the attendance of General
Yong-Lou in her temporary studio, under pretext of
giving him some official instructions.

The air was warm, the lake was limpid; cicadas,
hidden among the willows, sang an intoxicated hymn
to life, while the Son of Heaven, drunk as any coolie,
snored beatifically among his minions; the hour was
undeniably and eminently propitious.

Hardly had Yong-Lou, astonished and disturbed,
entered the delicately-shaded apartment, when
Ye-Ho-No-La, having hastily closed and bolted the
door, flung herself headlong into his arms.

She did so with all the fervour which she had
brought to the conquest of power, and happily Yong-
Lou, at twenty-two years of age and born of a fine
and lusty stock, proved a more than adequate partner

to his fiery mistress: Ye-Ho-No-La would scarcely have tolerated a second disappointment.

The words they said to one another and the vows they exchanged have remained unrecorded by History, but posterity has been able to ascertain that from that day onwards those two privileged beings lived always, as it were, in each other's hearts. Until death they remained faithful to their reciprocal undertakings and on numerous occasions saved each other's lives.

The Woman Who Commanded

In that pavilion of the Summer Palace where she gave herself over with passion to poetry, to painting, and to love, that is to say, to the most entrancing manifestations of life, Ye-Ho-No-La passed those hours which were, if not the most useful, at any rate the happiest of her reign.

Her exquisite beauty harmonised with surroundings of extreme luxury, and among the innumerable art treasures which adorned the imperial residence, she shone as the most perfect jewel.

As Dowager Empress she was later to evoke with tenderness the recollection of that ideal habitation where her spirit and her heart had thrilled in unison with her body. She was never to forget the earthly paradise where she knew for the first time all the raptures of love while revelling in the rarest enjoyment of art and literature. It was sheer ecstasy to her in the light mist of the summer dawns to float in her imperial barge on the blue waters of the magic lake; to hear the water fowl chasing each other among the reeds and the frogs perched upon the great lotus leaves chattering incessantly like so many concubines! How beautiful was the sky with its pink clouds floating above the gilded roofs of the pavilions!

Five Hundred Million Men

How sweetly the distant song of their silver bells harmonised with that of the cicadas hidden among the shimmering foliage of the willows on the banks!

And presently would come the fiery embrace in which an ardent body would receive the no less passionate caresses of a lover in the full sunshine of youth!

Triumphal mornings when love comes forth from the night as from a victory, when the blood burns in the veins and passion takes fire from the sunrise!

To be twenty-three years old in such a dream as this! What woman in all the world could ever have known such rapture!

But a tragic night was at hand when the divine heavens were to be obscured by sinister clouds; the doltish white-face Barbarians recalled Ye-Ho-No-La to grim reality.

Within twenty-four hours she had risen to the occasion with an energy worthy of the patrician blood in her veins. Tearing herself courageously from her idyll and thinking only of duty, she arose as the warlike inspiration of her menaced country, and savagely prepared for merciless conflict with the accursed sea-devils who had come to destroy the peace of the Celestial Empire. Quitting the Summer Palace, she returned to the Violet Town, daily assisting, from "behind the curtain," at the morning sittings of the Grand Council, at which Prince Kuong and his colleagues deliberated the measures to be adopted to repel the Barbarian aggression.

The Woman Who Commanded

The campaign opened with a victory: the plenipotentiaries of England and France, Lord Elgin and Baron Gros who, with their suites, had sought to force the Peï-Ho passes, had been repulsed by Tartar and Manchu troops under the command of the gallant General San-Ko-Li-Sien (1860). Unfortunately, instead of giving way at this first reverse, the accursed plenipotentiaries persevered in their diabolical intention of forcibly entering Peking.

The following year (1861) they returned with three hundred men-of-war and anchored at the mouth of the Peï-Ho.

In spite of a courageous defence offered by the Takou forts, the Barbarians succeeded in landing; then, pursuing their advance towards the capital, they successively overcame, at Tchang-Kiao-Wan and Pa-Li-Kiao, the army of San-Ko-Li-Sien, who had assured the Court that he was certain of victory.

With drawn swords and magnificent courage, the Tartar and Manchu cavalry vainly charged the accursed Barbarians; they were annihilated by artillery and rifle fire which mowed down their ranks with implacable precision. San-Ko-Li-Sien, in despair, fell back on Peking with the shattered remnants of a completely demoralised army.

The situation had now become exceedingly serious: the only available forces which remained to oppose the Barbarians were Yong-Lou's Imperial Manchu Guard, the supreme and final defence of a dynasty to

which only the Northern provinces had remained
faithful. As for the rest of the Celestial Empire,
it took no interest of any kind in the conflict, the
less so as Lord Elgin and Baron Gros had proclaimed
that they made war against the dynasty and not
against the Chinese people.

Moreover, Hong, the celebrated "celestial king,"
and his Taï-Ping, still occupied Nanking and retained
dominion over all the Yang-Tse-Kiang Valley in the
centre of China.

And finally, the Southern Chinese, and the Can-
tonese in particular, who still nourished a time-
honoured rancour against their Manchu masters, declared that much as they also detested the Barbarians,
they would be glad enough to see the fall of Peking.
At which juncture the Emperor Hien-Foung, who dis-
liked any interference with his debauches, cynically
announced that he intended to revive an ancient
custom and was leaving Peking in order to spend the
autumn hunting at Jehol, to the north of the capital.

At this news Ye-Ho-No-La overwhelmed the Son
of Heaven with a torrent of infuriated abuse that
recked nothing of traditional respect:

"Is this thing possible! That you, the representative of the great Manchu Tsin dynasty, should think
of running away like a common Chinese, basely
abandoning your capital to the Barbarians without
the slightest attempt at resistance? It is infamous
and shameful!"

The Woman Who Commanded

But the Holy Man, remaining quite unmoved, merely replied:

"I shall do exactly as I think best. Formerly, at this season of the year, my glorious predecessors were in the habit of going tiger-hunting. I shall therefore follow their illustrious precedent and shall admit of no sort of criticism."

And lending no further ear to the eloquent protests of the favourite, he gave orders that all preparations should be made for departure upon this remarkable hunting expedition.

Five Hundred Million Men

On the same day, at the Hour of the Horse, Ye-Ho-No-La hastily entered Prince Kuong's study.

The Emperor's brother appeared to be deeply perturbed: before him on the red lacquer table lay the decree in which the Son of Heaven officially informed his people that he was going to Jehol for the autumn hunting.

Ye-Ho-No-La exclaimed immediately:

"That decree must not be promulgated! . . . I appeal to your honour, Prince Kuong!"

He shook his head sadly:

"What can I do? My brother left this morning, accompanied by our cousins, Princes Tsaï-Youen and Touan-Houa, whose detestable influence over him you already know too well. They are now at the Summer Palace, the first stage of their northward journey. I am without legal power to arrest this grievous flight of the Son of Heaven! We may therefore just as well 'save our faces' by publishing this decree with regard to autumn hunting: the excuse is a poor one, as we know, but I do not see that I can invent a better!"

Ye-Ho-No-La demurred indignantly:

"We, the descendants of proud conquerors, have

85

not the right to betray our blood . . . let us fight to the death, and if we are beaten, let it be with our faces to the enemy! . . . As for me, I am quite determined to die in the foremost rank of the defenders of the Dragon's Throne. . . . But for that matter, who can be certain that fortune will not smile on our arms? . . . Peking is well victualled and able to withstand a long siege, and the ramparts of the Tartar Town can defy any artillery in the world. . . . Winter will come as a powerful auxiliary against these paleface Barbarians who are unaccustomed to such severe weather, and we may yet receive assistance from our loyal Northern provinces. . . ."

She continued to discourse exaltedly, outlining a military campaign and suggesting that the country people might be roused to refuse the invaders the necessary supplies for a long and arduous winter expedition. . . .

She was, in point of fact, perfectly right, and one wonders what might have happened to the Anglo-French forces if Ye-Ho-No-La had then been in a position to carry out her projects. It is obvious that the formidable ramparts of the Tartar Town could neither have been taken by assault nor demolished by artillery, while terrible fighting in the streets would have been only a prelude to the necessity of penetrating the triple defence of walls and moats of the final bastion enclosing the Forbidden City. Moreover, the Allies had already suffered severe losses, and it is likely that during the winter sickness and extreme cold would have further decimated the badly victualled and worse housed troops.

Moved to tears, Prince Kuong listened to the mother of the future Son of Heaven as she outlined the necessary measures to be taken for the final defence of the Dragon's Throne. But he could only reiterate:

"I am entirely powerless: my brother has taken with him to protect his flight all my available forces. . . . I am unable even to man the walls of Peking with enough troops to guard against a surprise attack."

He added:

"I shall not, however, leave my post. I shall remain in the Violet Town, even if I am to be buried in its ruins."

To which Ye-Ho-No-La replied proudly:

"And I, for my part, shall remain at your side!"

He looked at her with profound gratitude in his eyes: her conduct redeemed the cowardice of the Emperor Hien-Foung. But presently he replied in a voice of great regret:

"Your courage, Madam, is unquestionable, but your place is not here. You must follow after the Son of Heaven and prevent him if possible from any further display of cowardice or foolishness, and above all, it is your duty to watch over your son, the Heir Presumptive to the Throne, and thus to ensure the future of the dynasty. Much as it will cost you to go, you must hasten to rejoin the Court at the Summer Palace, there to be the guardian of such honour as remains in the imperial family."

Ye-Ho-No-La protested, but he did not cease to repeat:

"Painful as this course must be to you, Madam, it is clearly your duty! I adjure you, in the name of the dynasty, to perform it."

For a few moments Ye-Ho-No-La still hesitated, but she was compelled to recognise that Prince Kuong was right.

Bidding a regretful farewell to the generous prince who was so heroically replacing his unworthy brother, she set out with rage in her heart, to rejoin the Emperor Hien-Foung at the Summer Palace.

Five Hundred Million Men

Ye-Ho-No-La's imperial barge reached the lake before the Summer Palace just as night was falling. Never before had that enchanting spot appeared to her quite so beautiful.

The setting sun stained the sky above the curved gables and the shimmering tiles threw off a thousand sparkling fires. It was like a fairy illumination of the princely demesne, while upon the glowing waters of the lake floated innumerable dead leaves like copper butterflies. Great majestic swans glimmered like patches of silver in the mauve half-light among the lotus and reeds. Over there, behind the white marble balustrades, lay the graceful pavilion in which the young woman had found realisation of her fairest dreams of youth and love! What memories! It seemed to Ye-Ho-No-La as though her whole heart had remained imprisoned in this spot.

A curse upon the Barbarians who came to destroy this supreme masterpiece! Ye-Ho-No-La had slipped onto the marble junk which served as a landing stage, and was hastily making her way through the maze of pavilions that dotted the hillside.

Everything was in hideous disorder; a remnant of faithful retainers was seeking to collect and pack up the artistic treasures of the vast museum in order to save them from the greed of the Barbarians, who were now but a few hours' march from the imperial residence. Nearby a number of scared eunuchs were trying to restore order among a flock of terrified concubines.

Farther on, trembling ministers and shamefaced courtiers discussed the problem of their personal safety.

Finally, at the extreme end of the Summer Palace gaped open doors which afforded a view of the Northern road by which the imperial cortège would travel. It was already dotted with innumerable fugitives. The palace itself was a seething mass of servants of all sorts, actors, musicians, cooks and scullions jostled by soldiers who threw away their weapons in order to run more swiftly.

And not a soul paused to salute the mother of the Son of Heaven. Proudly and sadly, she made her way through the turmoil, her heart lacerated at the sight of so much shameful cowardice.

Outside the palace she beheld a large crowd surrounding a palanquin covered with yellow silk. Pitiably disguised as valiant sportsmen, the craven princes and a lamentable cohort of high dignitaries surrounded the Son of Heaven, who was going tiger-hunting while the enemy came to sack the shrine of his dynasty.

Five Hundred Million Men

Ye-Ho-No-La drew near. She raised the curtain of the litter and beheld the Holy Man, half drunk, toying with his minions in an effort to conceal his terror.

Nauseated, Ye-Ho-No-La let the curtain fall without attempting any appeal to the honour of the unworthy clown.

One single thought possessed her: she must find her son amid all this chaos and preserve him from the dangers of the retreat.

As she resumed her search she came across the cousins of the Son of Heaven, the Princes Tsaï-Youen and Touan-Houa, attired in marvellous hunting costumes.

She accosted them with exasperation:

"And what are you doing here? . . . Could you not have remained with Prince Kuong in the Violet Town? . . . Were you also afraid? . . ."

Their only reply was a shamefaced snigger.

Shrugging her shoulders, Ye-Ho-No-La pointed to a stout individual who, together with the princes, was giving careful attention to the transport of a load of gold ingots:

"And may I inquire the name of this valuable henchman?" she asked in sarcastic tones.

Whereupon Prince Touan-Houa thought fit to present his foster-brother, Sou-Chouen, who, thanks to his extortions, had contrived to amass the biggest

91

fortune in the Empire. Ye-Ho-No-La, who was fully aware of the scandalous manner whereby Sou-Chouen had become rich, merely remarked:

"I observe, sir, that in the midst of the general disorder, you at any rate have not lost your head . . . my congratulations!"

He excused himself hypocritically.

"If I have sought without delay to ensure the safety of this treasure, it is only because I hoped it might prove useful to the Court in exile."

The Princes Tsaï-Youen and Touan-Houa further emphasised:

"To us this gold may be indispensable."

And Ye-Ho-No-La turned on her heel with a grimace of disgust, and left them.

One thought still obsessed her: what had become of her son amid this chaos?

She addressed inquiries to all the fugitives that she met. They answered her only with vague gestures, for each had thought of himself alone and had no thought at all of the possible fate of the heir presumptive.

At length one of them volunteered the information that Ye-Ho-No-La would find her son safe in the care of the Empress Consort.

It was a fact that the Sovereign, placing the interests of the dynasty above any consideration of her personal sentiments, was jealously guarding the

Five Hundred Million Men

sole heir to the Throne, the son of a rival whom she had till that day viewed with abhorrence.

Here was a gesture that could not fail to touch the generous heart of Ye-Ho-No-La, who inwardly swore to leave nothing undone that could prove her gratitude to the Empress Consort.

She soon discovered that lady, in the very act of entering the carriage wherein she had previously installed the future Son of Heaven, together with her own daughter.

Ignoring the anarchy that surrounded them, the two august Sovereigns exchanged greetings with as much dignity as if they had met in the peace of the Violet Town: Ye-Ho-No-La thanked the Empress Consort affectionately and begged her graciously to forget their former estrangement. The Empress Consort overcame a visible hesitation, then she replied in a sad voice:

"Obviously, madam, our misfortune should unite us; let us set aside our personal grievances and think only of our common wish to protect the succession."

Ye-Ho-No-La rejoined impulsively:

"I shall in future always consider myself your debtor, and I beg that you will always look upon me as your most faithful and devoted ally!"

In this manner, amid a terrific catastrophe wherein the highest dignitaries completely lost their heads, did two young women display a grandeur of spirit only

93

to be equalled by the nobility of their common devotion to the Dragon's Throne.

For the honour of that imperial family that fled shamefully before the advancing foe, they displayed a courage and dignity that did indeed "save their faces"!

have got to admit it, we shall never prevail against the Barbarians until we can meet them with equal armaments. . . . That is the plain and simple truth!"

At those words Ye-Ho-No-La appeared to reflect deeply; presently she said:

"I thank you for your honesty, Yong-Lou; in better times, if Heaven permits it, I shall consider and endeavour to remedy our military inferiority."

He resumed:

"As for the Chinese, alas, we have never been able to depend on them!"

And these two fell to reviewing all the terrible revolts that had drenched the Celestial Empire in blood during recent years; they spoke of the innumerable Taï-Ping, entrenched in the very heart of China, and also of their indomitable leader, Hong, the Celestial King! They agreed that never had such a succession of calamities overwhelmed the entire land, and deplored the fact that at the very moment when the most energetic of sovereigns was required, the Dragon's Throne should be occupied by a pitiable degenerate!

Only Prince Kuong was really adequate to the situation, and what would become of him, alone in the Violet Town, almost certainly exposed to the direst violence on the part of the Barbarians! He was indeed a national hero! A pity that he was only the younger brother of the invertebrate Hien-Foung!

The Woman Who Commanded

While Ye-Ho-No-La and Yong-Lou were still conversing, they suddenly perceived a kind of phantom lurking among the shadows in the neighbourhood of the carriage. Yong-Lou sprang forward to intercept it and was already drawing his sword when to his great astonishment he recognised the Grand Eunuch, Ngan-Te-Hai.

Ye-Ho-No-La, who had also drawn near, inquired rather dryly:

"Are you perhaps under the impression that I am still the insignificant 'honourable person' whom it was your duty to watch over in her humble seclusion? Whom have you come to spy on?"

He bowed submissively:

"Forgive my anxious heart! I am in such fear that harm should befall you, Madam, in the midst of these hostile surroundings! . . . But I beg of you to believe that I am and shall always remain your humblest and most devoted servant."

Ye-Ho-No-La smiled sadly:

"And so you still love me! . . . Ah, my poor Ngan-Te-Hai, I am powerless in future to reward your devotion. . . ."

He exclaimed:

"But you will always be at liberty, I hope, to accept it! . . . Swear to me, Madam, that even in adversity, you will never exclude me from your trust."

Moved by so sincere an expression of loyalty at such a moment, Ye-Ho-No-La replied gently:

Five Hundred Million Men

"Most certainly, I shall always depend upon you in case of need . . . and I thank you for the assurance that I may trust you throughout any trials that may await me. . . . But for the moment, you may, without further anxiety, rejoin the concubines. . . . Yong-Lou is with me, and I have nothing to fear."

But even as she turned to smile at her celebrated lover, she beheld lurid clouds in the direction of the Summer Palace. Great flames leaped up, illuminating the entire horizon, and notably, with striking clearness, the hill upon which the Palace itself was built emerged as though in full daylight beneath a glowing sky. One by one, the wonderful pavilions that contained so many treasures, after appearing for a moment in black silhouette upon a flaming background, became enormous torches; columns of incandescent smoke arose, while a distant and ominous crackling sound could be distinguished. At intervals, moreover, gusts of hot wind brought, amid showers of sparks, the cries of the delirious white soldiers, bent upon the completion of the foulest outrage yet recorded by History. At this terrific spectacle, Ye-Ho-No-La almost lost her senses! She could not believe her eyes or conceive it possible that the accursed foreigners, debased though they might be, could have been so shameless as to stoop to such unparalleled ignominy.

They were, it seemed, not only Barbarians, but

veritable monsters! Truly the populace had done well to christen them "sea-devils"!

And Ye-Ho-No-La then and there registered a solemn vow never to forget this attack upon civilisation, this outrage against human evolution! All her life in future would be poisoned by an undying rancour, a savage hatred of the Occidental races!

Never again would she experience hours of perfect serenity, so constantly was she to be haunted by dreams of vengeance, even in the midst of her greatest triumphs. And yet, her hatred was obscured by an even stronger emotion, that of contempt; she utterly despised these boors who had respect neither for art, for beauty, nor even for love! And behind Ye-Ho-No-La stood six thousand years of cultured civilisation vomiting their disgust in the faces of the modern Vandals.

Five Hundred Million Men

CHAPTER TWENTY-THREE

After long and arduous days of journeying across almost deserted country, the miserable Court of the Emperor Hien-Foung had at length arrived at the ancient town of Jehol on the frontiers of Mongolia.

There was to end the pitiable farce of the tiger-hunt, improvised with a view to "saving the face" of a cowardly and ineffectual Son of Heaven exposed to the indignation of his people.

The imperial sportsmen had now no thought beyond that of finding, each for himself, tolerably comfortable quarters for the winter months.

But the ancient city had suffered neglect for so many years that the handsome hunting pavilions of bygone days were now nothing but tottering ruins with dilapidated and crumbling roofs.

A hasty effort was made to repair the least damaged of these abodes for the accommodation of the Holy Man and his personal suite. The flock of concubines were hurriedly parked in a species of worm-eaten barn, while the remainder of the Court sought shelter where it could be found, for the most part in veritable hovels.

What had become of the splendors of the Forbidden City and the luxuries of the Summer Palace?

However, the Holy Man continued to indulge in the lowest debauchery, in company with his first cousins, the Princes Tsaï-Youen and Touan-Houa, to whom was now added Sou-Chouen, foster-brother to the latter prince.

It was he who for the moment, thanks to the gold which he had brought along with him, afforded financial assistance to the impoverished Court, but he counted upon eventual repayment at compound interest and relied upon an adequate return for his calculating generosity. Already, with the support of his two allies, the Princes Tsaï-Youen and Touan-Houa, he was endeavouring to alienate the Emperor Hien-Foung from the still powerful influence of Ye-Ho-No-La.

Foreseeing the imminent demise of the Emperor, undermined by his excesses, the three accomplices were eager to achieve a prompt realisation of their ambitious projects.

Each day they invented a new scandal designed to prejudice the favourite in the eyes of the feeble-minded Holy Man; but they were powerless to diminish the affectionate trust that he retained for the mother of his only heir.

Ignoring the wretched intrigues of this trinity of scoundrels, Ye-Ho-No-La continued from afar to take an active part in the public affairs of the Celestial Empire.

Thanks to the unswerving devotion of the Grand

Eunuch Ngan-Te-Hai, who acted as her intermediary, she had contrived to keep in constant communication with Prince Kuong, who so valiantly remained at his post in the Violet Town.

With unspeakable joy she had learned that Hien-Foung's admirable brother had succeeded in protecting the Violet Town from the Barbarian outrages that had so tragically wrecked the Summer Palace. The Barbarians had entered the Town, but the self-possessed and diplomatic Prince Kuong had sown dissension between Lord Elgin and Baron Gros. The latter already deplored the disgraceful burning and still more shameful looting of the Summer Palace; he registered a formal opposition against any further outrage and finally persuaded his colleague to a wiser and more merciful course.

The treacherous ambush at Long-Chaou, which had trapped the emissaries Parks, Loch and d'Escayrac, undoubtedly called for exemplary retribution, but was it not almost equally vile to descend to the destruction of treasures of art in order to revenge these unfortunates even though they had been abominably tortured prior to their rescue by the victorious Allied troops?

In short, Lord Elgin in his turn agreed to clemency.

The peace treaty was now signed. The odious Barbarians were quitting Chinese territory, having gained nothing beyond a heavy indemnity and the empty satisfaction of having established at Peking the two ministers plenipotentiary representing England and France, Bruce and Bourboulon.

Of course it was understood that a small number of ports would remain open to foreign commerce, but that was a trifling concession and might moreover very possibly be turned to some advantage.

Prince Kuong, therefore, emerged triumphant from difficulties which had at first appeared insurmountable.

Most incredible of all was the fact that the Barbarians, who had in the first instance proclaimed that they had come to make war upon a dynasty and not upon China, had completely forgotten to carry out this interesting programme.

Not only this, but, urged thereto by the Shanghai merchants who were terrified at the growing successes of the Taï-Ping, the Barbarians now actually proffered their support to the shattered imperial government and amiably offered to undertake a campaign against Hong, the Celestial King, with a view to re-establishing in China the supremacy of the Peking government. Here was indeed unexpected good fortune! Prince Kuong might truly be considered the King of diplomats.

Ye-Ho-No-La rejoiced at the good news. She even forgave Prince Kuong for his failure to comply with the order she had given for the execution of all prisoners; he had in point of fact acted very wisely in giving them their freedom.

Deeply as she regretted the check to her first effort at vengeance on the Barbarians, she had enough diplomatic sense to realise that Prince Kuong was right.

A mutual trust cemented the alliance between the prince and Ye-Ho-No-La, and the future once more opened before them under the most happy auguries when a dramatic and unforeseen development suddenly upset all their calculations.

At the moment when the Court was preparing to leave Jehol and to return to Peking, the Emperor Hien-Foung became so gravely ill that the departure had to be postponed.

At which juncture the Princes Tsaï-Youcn and Touan-Houa, together with their accomplice, Sou-Chouen, redoubling their intrigues, at length contrived to persuade the dying Holy Man that he had been as thoroughly betrayed as the humblest of his subjects; they furnished him moreover with a wealth of details and did not forget to name the betrayer, General Yong-Lou, whom they cordially detested.

Although practically at death's door, the Holy Man revived sufficiently to fly into a violent fury with Ye-Ho-No-La. He proposed nothing less than to have her chopped into a thousand and one pieces by the Chief Executioner, if she could not contrive to exculpate herself.

Meanwhile he excluded her from his confidence and desired to deprive her of all those titles and prerogatives which pertained to her as mother of the heir presumptive.

Skilfully feeding the flame of his resentment, the conspirators obtained from the Holy Man *in extremis* a last decree conferring upon them the regency of the Celestial Empire during the minority of his successor.

Having committed this final imbecility, and displayed the blackest ingratitude, if not toward Ye-Ho-No-La, at any rate toward Prince Kuong, that excellent brother who had saved his Empire, the wretched Hien-Foung expired miserably among the noisy lamentations of his minions.

Fortunately for herself, and also for the Dragon's Throne, Ye-Ho-No-La had audaciously annexed the Seal of Transmitted Legitimate Authority without which no imperial decree could become law, and she was not the woman to surrender tamely that imposing seal which was her only protection from her adversaries. These last, still cowed by her indomitable courage, dared not employ force in order to regain possession of the Imperial Seal; they preferred to temporise, while secretly determining the murder of Ye-Ho-No-La upon the first favourable occasion.

In the meantime they decided that failing the official seal, the imperial decree remained operative, and proceeded to proclaim themselves legitimate Regents of the Celestial Empire during the minority of the young Son of Heaven who would reign under the name of Toung-Tche.

For her part, Ye-Ho-No-La judged it wiser at first to feign apparent submission. While careful to retain the Seal of Transmitted Legitimate Authority, she pretended to acknowledge as well-founded the pretensions of the three Regents.

But secretly, with the aid of the Grand Eunuch, Ngan-Te-Hai, she kept Prince Kuong informed of the gravity of their common political peril, begging him to act accordingly in Peking and to rouse up public opinion in their favour.

CHAPTER TWENTY-FOUR

Although it had been midwinter when the Emperor Hien-Foung had ascended the Dragon's Chariot, it was not until the second day of the ninth moon that the funeral procession, escorting his mortal remains, set out for Peking.

It had been necessary to await the preparation of an enormous catafalque designed to cover the coffin, and this had been by no means easy to construct in so out of the way a place as Jehol. Sou-Chouen, who had proclaimed himself co-Regent with the Princes Tsaï-Youen and Touan-Houa, had expedited the preparations and financed the enterprise.

What cared he! He felt safe to reap his sowing a hundred-fold now that he and his two accomplices had abrogated autocratic power. It was certainly not the new five-year-old Holy Man who would oppose their ambitious pretensions. Quite the reverse, his official Holiness afforded them protection, since all decrees would be promulgated in his name.

There was but one fly in the ointment: the whereabouts of the Seal of Transmitted Legitimate Authority, purloined by Ye-Ho-No-La, could not even yet be discovered. It would, however, ere long be simple enough to regain possession of it.

Five Hundred Million Men

The Regents deemed it prudent to avoid the public scandal that would be aroused by forcibly compelling Ye-Ho-No-La to restore the precious seal; they had therefore decided to achieve their object by more subtle means.

With this end in view, they did not shrink from the idea of compelling Ye-Ho-No-La to ascend the Dragon's Chariot before her destined hour, together with the Empress Consort who had remained her ally and would bear her company on the long voyage to the Yellow Fountains.

They therefore with extreme politeness begged the two Sovereigns graciously to precede them on the road to Peking in order that they might, as custom demanded, prepare for the return of the late Hien-Foung to his capital.

This was so entirely in accordance with the most time-honoured traditions that the two women had no hesitation in acceding to the request.

The three Regents bade them a pompous farewell and wished them an auspicious journey, having meanwhile with shameless treachery posted an entire band of assassins in the celebrated Kou-Pe-Keou defile. These assassins, who in the public eye would appear as ordinary robbers, were to attack, murder and plunder the noble travellers. In this oblique fashion did the Regents intend to regain possession, discreetly and without scandal, of the famous Seal of Transmitted Legitimate Authority which Ye-Ho-No-La still bore jealously concealed in her bosom.

It went without saying that after the outrage, the three accomplices were prepared to utter noisy lamentations and even to accord their victims magnificent funerals which should further avert suspicion.

Sou-Chouen sniggered:

"This will mean yet another hole in my personal finances, but one must be prepared to make small sacrifices in life if one is to maintain one's social position."

And the other Regents admired their colleague's subtle humour.

Meanwhile, the two women having left Jehol, these scoundrels serenely set out to follow the enormous catafalque which covered the coffin of the Holy Man, with difficulty borne by one hundred and twenty bearers.

Together with the three Regents, the poor little new Holy Man also followed, with a gravity that sat oddly on his five years, the mortal remains of his predecessor.

The procession advanced slowly through a mourning countryside; it would be more than a moon before it could hope to sight the high walls of Peking. But what matter! Between now and then the three Regents would have time and to spare in which to affix to the decree of the late Hien-Foung appointing them to the Regency, the Seal of Transmitted Legitimate Authority, fortunately recovered from the corpse of Ye-Ho-No-La. Who would then dare to murmur against their Regency, confirmed by unquestionable authority? Possibly the brothers of the late Emperor Hien-Foung, the Princes Kuong and Tchouen? But the Regents would make short work of coping with their opposition and had even conceived the project of having them put to death, together with any other members of the imperial family who might prove unfriendly.

But the Grand Eunuch Ngan-Te-Hai, who never ceased from jealously guarding the safety of Ye-Ho-No-La, had got wind of the conspiracy. A few fragments of conversation, overheard at Jehol, had awakened his suspicions, and by patiently spying upon every word and gesture of the conspirators, he had managed to acquire knowledge of the frightful truth.

Whereupon, without saying a word to anyone, he at once deserted his post as leader of the flock of concubines who followed their late lord as official mourners, and galloped off at top speed to General Yong-Lou.

The latter, when his intimacy with Ye-Ho-No-La had been treacherously betrayed to the Emperor Hien-Foung, had left Jehol and was in Manchuria rallying his old companions-in-arms.

He had already succeeded in forming a considerable army, when he was joined by the Grand Eunuch who at once hastened to inform him of the grave situation.

Whereupon Yong-Lou galloped off without drawing rein and followed by all his faithful Manchu cavalry made post haste for the Kou-Pe-Keou pass in which his beloved was to be foully murdered. He was a prey to intense emotion, having calculated that he had barely time to reach Kou-Pe-Keou before the hour fixed for the abominable outrage.

It was a headlong dash across valley and mountain! The terrified peasants beheld the thunderous passing of these savage warriors who uttered fierce cries in order to urge their galloping horses to yet greater speed.

A very few seconds' delay would, in point of fact, have altered the entire course of History in the Far East!

Already the band of assassins posted by the three Regents had leaped forth upon the feeble escort that accompanied the Empress and Ye-Ho-No-La, and were pitilessly murdering those few defenders who stood their ground, when, as though by a miracle, they were overwhelmed by an immense charge of valiant Manchu horsemen. In the twinkling of an eye, mowing down the wretched assassins, they cleared a space round the carriages in which the Sovereigns were awaiting inevitable death, and Yong-Lou leaped forward to ascertain whether Ye-Ho-No-La was safe and sound.

But she, with admirable self-possession, had descended from her carriage and with seemly and traditional solemnity, proffered her thanks to her official saviour in whom she secretly greeted the ever faithful lover.

The Woman Who Commanded

CHAPTER TWENTY-FIVE

Closely guarded by Yong-Lou's troops, the two Sovereigns soon arrived safely in Peking, where they hastened to the residence of Prince Kuong.

The three of them lost no time in formulating a decree which conferred upon them a joint Regency during the minority of the Son of Heaven, who would reign under the name of Toung-Tche. By a pleasant fiction, this decree was moreover attributed to the five-year-old Holy Man, and was regarded as immediately operative, since Ye-Ho-No-La was able to adorn it with the impression of the Seal of Transmitted Legitimate Authority which she had so courageously retained, even at the risk of her life.

There remained only to await calmly the arrival of the funeral cortège of the late Emperor Hien-Foung, formally escorted by the three accomplices in the usurpation of power.

If the truth must be told, these latter were beginning to be extremely anxious, for Ye-Ho-No-La, with malicious irony, had contrived to inform them by special messenger that she had had an entirely pleasant journey and trusted that theirs would be equally auspicious. Not a word about the ambush which they had prepared! But the conspirators were not deceived. Nevertheless, with a certain audacity, they did not seek to escape, but put as good a face as possible on the situation and stuck to their astounding adventure.

On the second day of the tenth moon, the funeral procession at length arrived before the great Northern Gates of the Tartar Town. An immense crowd thronged the walls, which are so wide that several chariots could pass along them abreast. From afar, one might have thought that a great blue scarf was laid along the summit of the vast grey stones which form these prodigious defences. Meanwhile, Toung-Tche, the five-year-old Holy Man, had solemnly taken his place near the Great Gate beneath a specially erected canopy, there to receive the coffin of his illustrious sire. Beside him, draped in mourning, were his mother, Ye-Ho-No-La, the Empress Consort and the brothers of the late Emperor Hien-Foung, the Princes Kuong and Tchouen, together with other members of the imperial family. As prescribed by ritual, the three usurping Regents detached themselves for a moment from the funeral procession, in order to report their mission in traditional manner to the new Son of Heaven. Bowing profoundly, they performed the prescribed genuflexions before the youthful deity.

As though petrified into stately immobility, the Sovereigns and Prince Kuong gravely observed the ceremony; their eyes never wavered, not a muscle

115

of their faces moved, they might have been lifeless statues.

Among the crowd which pressed around the daïs, not a soul was permitted to suspect the tumultuous emotions of their hearts. In his childish voice, the new Holy Man, lisping the words he had with difficulty memorised, thanked the three mock Regents for having so successfully accomplished their mission. He then proceeded with the funeral oration, of which he would have made a hopeless muddle, had not his careful mother, Ye-Ho-No-La, prompted him with all the traditional epithets. Finally, having laboriously accomplished his task, he clambered off the funeral daïs in order to accompany the imperial coffin into the Forbidden City.

At this juncture, the three usurpers, with consummate impudence, arrogantly invited Prince Kuong and the Sovereigns to take their places behind them in the funeral procession.

Whereupon Ye-Ho-No-La, who had bided her time, inquired in trenchant tones:

"Who is it dares to issue such a command?"

The Princes Tsaï-Youen and Touan-Houa answered dryly:

"You cannot be unaware, Madam, since you yourself recognised the fact at Jehol, that we, together with Sou-Chouen, are joint Regents of the Celestial Empire. Such was the last command of the **Holy Man**, Hien-Foung."

"That is a question which will here and now be debated," replied Ye-Ho-No-La. "Where is the decree which confirms your claim?"

Unabashed, they proffered the imperial decree.

Ye-Ho-No-La immediately exclaimed:

"Behold the imposture of these ruffians! This parchment lacks the imprint of the Seal of Transmitted Legitimate Authority."

And seizing another decree, extended by Prince Kuong, she proceeded:

"Here is the only decree that is valid, since it bears the imperial seal. I appeal to all here present, princes of the blood, ministers and high dignitaries, for loyal support!"

Whereupon, as though by the merest hazard, the loyal Manchus of Yong-Lou's Guard appeared from all directions, ostentatiously drawing their swords from the scabbards.

At this sight the adherents of the usurping Regents began quietly to fade away.

Ye-Ho-No-La resumed:

"It is, therefore, I who assume command, jointly with the Empress Consort and Prince Kuong, and I direct you to take your places behind us in the funeral procession."

Pale to the lips, the conspirators realised that the game was up. It had become futile to attempt any further bluff.

Outwardly composed, they bowed and replied:

"In order to avoid scandal, it shall be as you suggest."

Utterly discomfited, they joined the funeral procession in the subsidiary places allotted them by Ye-Ho-No-La.

And never for a moment did the populace thronging the walls of the Tartar Town suspect that a great coup d'état had been accomplished before their very eyes. With perfect self-possession and seemliness, all the members of the imperial family, who had so recently crossed swords, accompanied the coffin of the Emperor Hien-Foung to the Throne Room where it was solemnly left to await the official funeral. There was moreover a lengthy closing ceremony in which all those present vied with each other in minute observance of the thousand and one rules of a terribly complicated etiquette. A common and edifying sorrow appeared to unite all the members of the august family, who mutually exchanged with extreme punctilio all the salutations decreed by century-old tradition.

It was not until the Princes Tsaï-Youen and Touan-Houa were about to depart, followed by their trembling accomplice, Sou-Chouen, that they were discreetly approached by General Yong-Lou.

The three mock Regents started at recognising the inveterate adversary whom they had actually condemned to death and whom they had intended promptly to execute.

Five Hundred Million Men

With the greatest calm Yong-Lou began by bowing ceremoniously to the three impostors, then he suggested with infinite courtesy:

"Your Highnesses will be so good as to follow me."

But he added in a threatening undertone:

"Obey! Resistance would be quite useless!"

The three accomplices became livid with terror; all around them, guarding every exit from the Forbidden City, were Yong-Lou's soldiers with drawn swords.

A faint hope remained, however: was it possible that these warriors, all of Manchu race, might not dare to assault members of the imperial family who must surely remain sacred in their eyes?

It seemed that a slight hesitation oppressed them.

But they had all reckoned without an unforeseen stroke of genius.

Ye-Ho-No-La, who had had her misgivings, suddenly appeared on the threshold of the mortuary chamber, accompanied by the new Holy Man! Seizing the child in her arms, she held him up to the Manchu soldiers.

"Here is your Emperor!" she cried in ringing tones. "He commands you to obey his mother and to swear fidelity to her as you would to his own sacred Person!"

Her words evoked an uproar of cheers and enthusiasm! All the soldiers waved their weapons wildly and thronged to salute their Emperor and his Divine Mother!

The Woman Who Commanded

At which impressive spectacle the Princes Tsaï-Youen and Touan-Houa realised that no power on earth could now avert their doom.

Turning to Yong-Lou, they addressed him in faltering accents.

"It is well. . . . We will follow you, wherever you choose to lead us."

A few moments later they were ushered into the prison reserved for important offenders in the fastnesses of the Forbidden City.

The doors closed upon them and they heard the heavy bolts shot home that severed them for ever from the outside world.

Five Hundred Million Men

CHAPTER TWENTY-SIX

On the very next morning following that memorable day, Ye-Ho-No-La and the Empress Consort took their seats in the Grand Council Chamber, behind the yellow silk curtain that traditionally screened their Majesties. As soon as they were comfortably installed upon their thrones of state, they signified that the Audience might begin.

Prince Kuong was the first to enter the Chamber and perform the customary genuflexions before the "lowered curtain"; he was succeeded by the other members of the Grand Council who executed the same contortions. The eunuchs, who stood beside their Sovereigns, observed the ceremony through special openings in the curtain, and reported thereon to their respective mistresses.

Ngan-Te-Hai, who was privileged to assist Ye-Ho-No-La, could scarcely contain himself with pride and joy: anyone might have thought that he himself was to be proclaimed Supreme Lord of the Celestial Empire. It was true that his had been a narrow escape. If he had, on the one hand, been instrumental in saving his mistress' life, on the other hand, failing the amazing energy displayed by that extraordinary woman, he would most assuredly have been condemned to a lingering death by the Princes Tsaï-Youen and Touan-Houa, who would never have forgiven his behaviour.

Prince Kuong opened the meeting of the Grand Council by immediately requesting from the other members confirmation of his powers as Regent, jointly with Ye-Ho-No-La and the Empress Consort.

It was then solemnly determined that Ye-Ho-No-La, who, all-powerful favourite though she had been, had only held the official position of "fei" concubine, should in future rank as Empress, equally with the Empress Consort. Ye-Ho-No-La should now be entitled the Empress Tseu-Hi, which is to say "maternal and propitious" Empress, while the Empress Consort should assume the titles of Tseu-Ngan; which being interpreted denotes "maternal and peaceful" Empress.

The former should be Empress of the Palace of the West, the latter Empress of the Palace of the East.

Both should wield supreme authority concurrently with Prince Kuong, throughout the minority of the Holy Man, Toung-Tche. Further, a civil pension of several hundred million taels was voted to their Majesties, and the meeting closed amid enthusiastic vows of fidelity.

It need hardly be emphasised that everyone was well aware, in view of the character of the two Empresses, that the true Sovereign would in future be the Mother of the august Son of Heaven.

Five Hundred Million Men

Prince Kuong himself had determined to accept the supremacy of Tseu-Hi, of whom he deeply admired the energy and intelligence while he was captivated by her radiant beauty and subtle wit.

The die was therefore cast: the erstwhile poor little concubine, Ye-Ho-No-La, who ten years ago had so humbly entered the imperial harem in the Violet Town, had become the glorious Empress Tseu-Hi, omnipotent mistress of the vastest Empire in the Universe.

At twenty-six years of age this extraordinary Sovereign held absolute sway of life and death over five hundred million subjects! And she was destined to exercise this stupendous authority for more than half a century, without anyone daring to contest it.

What destiny indeed was ever equal to hers since the beginning of the world! What other super-woman can any historian oppose to the illustrious Empress Tseu-Hi!

PART TWO

THE EMPRESS TSEU-HI

CHAPTER ONE

One of the earliest official acts of the Empress Tseu-Hi was to arraign before the Chamber of the Grand Council the imperial Princes Tsaï-Youen and Touan-Houa and their acolyte, Sou-Chouen.

There ensued a manifestation of her amazing faculty for conducting herself, if such a term may be applied to a woman, in a truly statesmanlike manner. Instead of dwelling on the murderous attack upon her person designed by her late political adversaries, she passed over this offence in silence, ignoring her undoubted claims to retribution. She was determined that the judgment which she demanded should have no colouring of personal revenge.

From the very outset of her reign she desired to convey the impression that nothing counted with her beside the good of the State and the Honour of the Dynasty. It was therefore on a simple charge of high treason that she caused the culprits to be arraigned before their peers, the other members of the imperial family, to whom were added the ministers and high officials.

With passive dignity, disdaining the personal outrages to which she had been subjected, the Empress

127

Tseu-Hi instituted a strenuous process, worthy of a brilliant lawyer, against the offenders.

She recalled their selfish cowardice when the Barbarians had been at the gates of the capital. She established beyond the possibility of doubt the sinister influence which they had at that time exercised over the vacillating mind of the Emperor Hien-Foung, and she concluded by a judicial contention that their entire conduct had been contrary not only to the laws of honour, but also to the interests of the Son of Heaven and of the Celestial Empire.

Traitors to their Sovereign, traitors to their country, traitors also to the noble blood which ran in their veins; such was the pitiless conclusion of an accusation firmly based upon incontestable facts of which Tseu-Hi had herself been a nauseated witness.

Finally, there had been added the damning circumstance that, not content with such a record of ill-doing, they had ignominiously sought to usurp authority in order to complete their shameful and ruinous work. The deliberation of the members of the Grand Council was brief. They unanimously acknowledged the charges to be well founded, and in the name of the Holy Man, who nominally presided over their proceedings, they promulgated the following judgment:

"Deeply impressed by the incredible succession of misdemeanours, by the crimes of high treason and usurpation of authority of which the Princes Tsaï-

Youen and Touan-Houa have been guilty, together with their detestable accomplice, Sou-Chouen, We decree that our Grand Executioner shall put them to a lingering death, by cutting into a thousand pieces the bodies of these three criminals whose existence brings shame upon our Family.

"Their goods shall be forfeited to the State and the names of their families erased from the Imperial genealogy.

"May their terrible example serve as a lesson to any who may be tempted to emulate these traitors! Reverence to this!"

Having thus obtained ample satisfaction of her legitimate desires for vengeance, Ye-Ho-No-La might well have been content simply to endorse the judgment of the Members of the Grand Council, allowing affairs to take their most rigorous course. But she judged it more politic, as well as more becoming, to inaugurate her reign by an unprecedented act of mercy. Of her own responsibility, thus assuming supreme power, she promulgated in the name of the Holy Man, a fresh decree in which it was announced that, while the judgment of the Members of the Grand Council was approved and upheld, in view of their rank as members of the imperial family, the Princes Tsaï-Youen and Touan-Houa would be granted the unprecedented favour, in spite of their heinous guilt, of being their own executioners.

As for Sou-Chouen, he would merely be beheaded,

but might expect no further clemency. In obedience to this new decree, the Princes Tsaï-Youen and Touan-Houa therefore obtained the unhoped-for opportunity of escape from the terrible "lingering death." They thankfully hastened to hang themselves with the yellow silk bowstrings which were ceremoniously presented to them in a coffret of red lacquer.

As for Sou-Chouen, it was with equal relief that he gladly extended his neck to the executioner's sword.

On the other hand, all his worldly goods and those of his family remained forfeit to the Dragon's Throne, forming the foundations of the immense personal fortune later accumulated by the Empress Tseu-Hi.

As a further diplomatic evidence of clemency, however, she refrained from permanently excluding from the Imperial Clan the relations of the Princes Tsaï-Youen and Touan-Houa; by this action she acquired devoted adherents in the place of incurring secret animosities among these noble families.

Finally, instead of savagely persecuting those high functionaries who had compromised themselves on behalf of the conspirators, they were joyfully surprised at finding themselves merely superseded. She thus at trifling cost acquired a great reputation for wisdom and clemency which made her immensely popular with all classes of the people. She was no longer merely the Empress whose lightest wish was jealously respected; she became a veritable idol and the recipient of divine honours. Tseu-Hi soon learned that her grateful country had accorded her the title of "old buddha," in which it found expression for both its love and its respect.

The epithet "old" might have brought a smile to the lips of this lovely young woman, had she not known that it was the most honourable title that could be conferred upon her youth, and carried with it the most subtle of compliments.

Each country possesses its customs which it would be vain to criticise.

CHAPTER TWO

Taking advantage of the momentary eclipse of the Peking Government and of the flight of the Court to Jehol, the Taï-Ping had made themselves absolute masters of Central China. Hong, their "celestial king," posed as emperor in Nanking, the Southern capital, and his authority extended to Shanghai, that gigantic metropolis of all commerce in the Far East.

There existed therefore in practice, if not theoretically, a State within a State, and the Celestial Empire could not aspire to peace pending the abolition of this anomaly.

The Empress Tseu-Hi was perfectly well aware of the danger offered to the entire country as well as to the dynasty by this formidable insurrection which had been steadily growing in strength for over ten years. Entire cities had been sacked and burned by the terrible Taï-Ping; the panic-stricken peasants deserted their untilled fields beneath a reign of terror and triumphant brigandage. The valiant general Cheng-Kouo-Fang whom Tseu-Hi had sent to oppose the Taï-Ping barely contrived to hold his positions, and Li-Houng-Tchang, the astute viceroy of Kiang-Sou, had beheld the invasion of his territory and could barely sustain a desperate struggle to blockade the rebels on the road to Shanghai. Unless some new factor could be brought into play, the situation appeared well-nigh hopeless.

It was at this juncture that the Empress Tseu-Hi proved herself really adequate to her task. Controlling her hatred for the accursed paleface Barbarians who had so recently lacerated her heart by sacking her marvellous Summer Palace, she ably invited their co-operation in the struggle against the Taï-Ping, and there arose an amazing state of affairs: the sea-devils who had come from the far distant Occident to overthrow the Manchu dynasty, turned to the right-about and entered the lists against the enemies of the Dragon's Throne. This was a triumph of diplomacy largely due, it must be admitted, to the ingenuity of Li-Houng-Tchang.

This Chinese of ancient lineage had in the first place received a very reluctant welcome from the Empress Tseu-Hi, who had never till then admitted any but Manchus to prominent distinction. But necessity knows no law: Li-Houng-Tchang, having known how to ingratiate himself with the paleface Barbarians, had become an indispensable intermediary between these and the Court at Peking.

As a matter of fact the Europeans were growing doubtful as to whether the final success of the Taï-Ping would not be more adverse to their interests than the survival of the Manchu dynasty.

Hong, the "celestial king," was proving to be even

more savagely anti-foreign than the most extreme Northern nationalists. It was well known that should he gain possession of Shanghai the entire city would be sacked and no foreigner would be spared. France and England therefore agreed to oppose by armed force an invasion which would have had fatal results upon their commerce in the Far East. They had hastily formed a heterogeneous collection of diverse elements which the English wittily christened "the army ever victorious" in allusion to the bragging of the various adventurers of which it was composed. In it derelicts of every known white race were allied with vague Chinese mercenaries of all descriptions to form the most astounding army of history.

Naturally, the little "army ever victorious" obtained but very qualified successes against the Taï-Ping, since its discipline was non-existent and its soldiers thought only of sacking in their turn such villages as they snatched from the enemy.

The Empress Tseu-Hi, receiving a succession of gloomy reports from Li-Houng-Tchang in her Palace of Perpetual Spring, began to abandon all hopes of ever seeing the end of the Taï-Ping rebellion.

The French Rear-Admiral Protet, who had wished to gain immediate possession of Nanking by steaming up the Yang-Tse-Kiang with landing parties, had been killed under the walls of the Southern capital. Who could be depended upon in future, if even the bravest foreign warriors failed in their struggle against the "celestial king"!

Happily Li-Houng-Tchang did not lose courage. With untiring energy, recklessly spending millions of taels, he contrived to muster a real army, which on this occasion was well equipped and possessed of a reliable staff. Without delay he persuaded the English to give the command of this army to the celebrated General Gordon, that military genius who was later to meet at Khartoum in Upper Egypt a tragic end worthy of his astonishing adventurous career.

Swallowing the affront to her pride, the Empress Tseu-Hi accepted General Gordon as commander-in-chief of her army. Under the control of this great leader of men, the campaign against the Taï-Ping quickly changed its aspects. The enemy were attacked with method and discipline, and very soon their principal chiefs, surrounded at Sou-Cheou, the capital of the Kiang-Sou, were forced to lay down their arms. A hundred thousand men, a mass of artillery, and a vast amount of specie fell into Gordon's hands.

A few days would have completed the conquest of the Taï-Ping when there occurred a most unfortunate incident.

General Gordon was a chivalrous hero; he had been the first to deplore the sack of the Summer Palace, and he wished, as the honourable conqueror of courageous adversaries, to maintain magnanimity in conquest. He had therefore given his word of honour as a soldier to the Taï-Ping leaders that their lives should be spared if they capitulated in Sou-Cheou. What was therefore the indignation of this gallant gentleman on learning that Li-Houng-Tchang, in defiance of all decency, had accomplished the massacre of all the prisoners.

Mad with fury, he set off to find the viceroy, in order to blow out his brains, but he was unable to discover the whereabouts of the crafty mandarin who had prudently sought concealment.

Gordon was forced to content himself with a grand gesture: he proudly returned to Peking the treasure bestowed upon him in gratitude for his victory, and breaking his sword, he departed from the Celestial Empire in deep disgust.

His departure in no way disturbed the Empress Tseu-Hi, who, now that he had accomplished the main portion of his task, was, in point of fact, not sorry to see the back of the great Barbarian leader.

She therefore afforded Li-Houng-Tchang the support of her authority, and merely ordered him to complete General Gordon's work. The Taï-Ping had been both decimated and thoroughly demoralised by the thunderous victories of the English hero, and only a faithful remnant were gathered round Hong the "celestial king" at Nanking. Li-Houng-Tchang ordered General Cheng-Kouo-Fang to assist him in subduing this final resistance, and the siege of Nanking was eagerly undertaken.

A happily placed mine succeeded in making a breach in the walls. The imperial soldiery poured into it and put to the sword without quarter all the defenders of the town.

Following up this successful enterprise, Li-Houng-Tchang and Cheng-Kouo-Fang recaptured all the territory occupied by the Taï-Ping. With implacable ferocity they drowned the remnants of insurrection in torrents of blood.

Appalling massacres took place and all those who were even suspected of sympathy with the Taï-Ping were slaughtered to the last man. Order now reigned supreme throughout the Celestial Empire and rebellion hid its terrified head in all the provinces. The Empress Tseu-Hi had become absolute and uncontested mistress of all her subjects.

She enthusiastically conferred on General Cheng-Kouo-Fang and on Li-Houng-Tchang the highest titles of nobility and loaded them with costly gifts, but she caused it to be officially proclaimed in accordance with the established tradition, that their sensational success was due to the Spirit of Hien-Foung! History does not relate whether she repressed a smile while drafting this honourable and traditional decree. There followed great fêtes at Peking, to celebrate the annihilation of the Taï-Ping, the culminating rejoicing being caused by the arrival in that city of the cage containing the leaders of that body, captured at Nanking. The captives were vivisected slowly into a thousand pieces on the Place of Execution in the Chinese Quarter of Peking close to the walls of the Tartar Town. The execution took place in the presence of an immense crowd who thoroughly enjoyed the marvellous entertainment, only regretting that Hong, the "celestial king," was not there to enact the principal part in so pleasing a drama. But he, realising that the game was up, had prudently swallowed poison at Nanking, before the final assault by the imperial forces.

Five Hundred Million Men

The storm which had so severely swept over the Celestial Empire had suddenly abated, giving place to a flat calm. Not a cloud obscured the horizon, and, contrary to all expectations, the dynasty issued from the turmoil strengthened and as it were rejuvenated. The paleface Barbarians had vanished, the Taï-Ping had ceased to exist, order reigned throughout the land and an era of prosperity succeeded years of anarchy and discord. At Court, as among the imperial family, there was peace and concord; the palace intrigues had ceased, vain ambitions no longer flourished. The Empress Tseu-Hi was able in all composure of mind to wield absolute authority without encountering the slightest opposition, and was even at liberty to indulge her every caprice. Her co-regent, the Empress Tseu-Ngan, voluntarily abstained from public life, desirous only of leading a peaceful existence in her Palace of the East surrounded by her eunuchs and retainers.

As for Prince Kuong, he applied himself daily with admirable conscientiousness to the current affairs of State, thus exempting Tseu-Hi from all material anxiety. He always, however, loyally solicited her advice, courteously ceding to her the foremost place

139

in the government. All was therefore for the best
in the best of all possible worlds, and Tseu-Hi with
rapture now aspired only to full enjoyment of her
marvellous destiny. She had everything that woman
could desire: power, youth, charm and beauty; she
was free and wealthy and rejoiced moreover in perfect health and superabundant vitality. She was
careful not to abuse these precious advantages,
though she tasted voluptuously all the joys of
existence, satisfying her mind, her body and her
heart; she displayed as much ardour in her pleasures
as she had shown energy in misfortune. Her many
passions were insatiable and her enthusiasm burned
equally, whether she was delicately wielding a brush
for the composition of exquisite verses or for the
delineation of delightful water-colours, whether she
dreamed strange, opium-tinted dreams, sampled rare
dishes, acted plays in company with the Grand
Eunuch before an amazed audience of aged Court
officials, or found heaven in the arms of her faithful
Yong-Lou. All of which never prevented her, when
need arose, from being the most far-seeing and level-
headed of Sovereigns or from presiding with incomparable dignity at the meetings of the Grand Council.
She did not in fact ever abandon herself to any excess that might have lowered her; she was dignified
even in her most intimate transports and retained her
nobility in the most questionable situations.

Had she chosen to wallow in the mire she would

have remained the undefilable pearl of great price. An aristocrat to the tips of her fingers, it may almost be said that she exalted vice itself. It was indeed one of her greatest pleasures to overwhelm with her irresistible sarcasm those virtuous official censors who, in conformity with age-old customs, approached her with traditional remonstrances. She would at first pretend to take them seriously, thanking them effusively for their wise advice, and would end the interview by the promulgation of a decree authorising one or another of these ancients to retire into well-earned seclusion and pleasantly suggesting a retreat to a home and family who would tend the ailments of encroaching age.

She thus made drastic breaches in the composition of the Tribunal of Rites and the Court of Censors, wreaking an apparently unpremeditated havoc among these ancient institutions which she regarded as incompatible with her ardent youth. Her seeming carelessness concealed a deliberate determination to act as she pleased in any circumstances and to allow of no check upon her caprices.

When one is at the same time the loveliest woman and the most powerful individual in a vast empire, it would indeed be foolish to tolerate the merest shadow of restraint! And since imagination was not the least developed of Tseu-Hi's many rare qualities, she knew how to instil variety not only into her pleasures, but into her manner of enjoying them. And could anyone have been so hard-hearted as to blame her!

Was she not completely within her rights, since she had the capacity for combining such varied occupations without prejudice to State affairs and without diminution of her genius which, like her marvellous health, withstood every exaction.

Her reputation, moreover, remained irreproachable; the populace continued to speak with affection of the "old buddha" whom Heaven had happily and mercifully set for salvation at the head of the Celestial Empire. Not a suspicion disturbed their touching and simple faith; their adoration knew no bounds.

Obviously, had they been able to explore the interior of the shrine, they might have been somewhat nonplussed at certain rather questionable episodes in their idol's career, but the Forbidden City remained discreetly immune from all inquisitive eyes. When a ruler assumes divine attributes it is wise and proper that a certain mystery should surround the Throne!

This fact has always been clearly comprehended by Asiatic autocrats, be it in China, Korea or Japan, and furnishes a natural explanation of the mystical veneration in which the people have always held their rulers.

When one claims to be the representative of Heaven on earth it is imprudent, not to say unseemly, to exhibit a commonplace human countenance before the general public. It is quite sufficient to be exposed to the skeptical eyes of those high priests who are, in any case, foremost among unbelievers.

The Empress Tseu-Hi was far too intelligent ever to commit such a blunder, and while well aware that she might with impunity have risked any indiscretions, she contrived skilfully to mask her personality behind a screen of convention and etiquette. It was for this reason that she invariably sat behind the "lowered curtain" when presiding at the sittings of the Grand Council.

Even in contact with her ministers, she considered it opportune to veil her august countenance, which did not prevent her, a few hours later in the inviolable retreat of her Palace of Perpetual Spring, from passionately offering her ardent lips to the kisses of Yong-Lou.

The Woman Who Commanded

CHAPTER FOUR

The barge draped in yellow silk which bore the Empress Tseu-Hi made its way with difficulty through the rushes and water plants which had invaded the lake before the long deserted Summer Palace. Thousands of wild birds flew off, uttering piercing cries, but the stately swans of bygone days were no longer there to mirror themselves in the placid waters.

A dense tangle of undergrowth smothered the banks, with the exception of that portion upon which had formerly stood the wonderful pavilions of the imperial residence. Here the ground offered a bare and desolate aspect: it was littered with a thousand calcined fragments, a chaos of broken tiles and charred beams extended to the summit of the hill. Here and there an isolated white marble column had remained standing and was reflected in the blue lake; the remainder of the adorable Summer Palace was a smoke-blackened, shattered heap of ruins, utterly destroyed by the criminal hands of the odious Barbarians.

At this sight, Tseu-Hi, who had not before revisited these shores, was unable to restrain a tear which slid slowly down her lovely face, like a pearl of great price. It was in fact the only tear that was ever shed by that energetic Sovereign, who throughout her entire life knew how to preserve an impassive exterior even in the most tragic circumstances. It was for that very reason that this solitary tear was so infinitely distressing and that the Grand Eunuch, Ngan-Te-Hai, who accompanied his mistress, was so profoundly moved.

How deeply she must be suffering thus to betray her pain! Never before had he seen her weep, and he had hardly believed her capable of tears. She was usually so proud, so strong, so sure of herself! Preserving a respectful silence, he sadly bent his head as though in discreet homage to her mourning heart.

And Tseu-Hi, observing his gesture, was infinitely grateful to him; truly this castrate had retained a rare delicacy of intuition and the beauty of his soul made it easy to forget that he had only the appearance of a genuine lover. Experiencing a sudden keen desire to confide her sorrow to one who would be capable of the subtlest understanding, Tseu-Hi said in gentle accents:

"I thank you, Ngan-Te-Hai, for having known how to convey to me your sorrowful sympathy. I am ashamed that I should have allowed a tear to escape me. . . . My rank, my blood, my character, all these forbade it, and yet I permitted my weakness to master me! . . . If you should ever tell anyone that you once beheld the Empress Tseu-Hi overcome by such emotion that she almost wept, no one, I know it,

145

would believe you. And yet that emotion was sincere and came from the bottom of my heart! Only you can have full knowledge of the dear memories which have vanished from me in the ashes of the Summer Palace. . . . With it went all my enthusiasm and my youthful hopes; in it I was gay, I was care-free, I was happy. It knew my youth and the coming to me of love, and all the best of me, of my heart and of my spirit, is buried here amid these ghastly ruins!"

She sighed deeply: before her anguished gaze, which she could not avert from the blackened hillside, passed a procession of pure and lovely bygone memories; the enchanting spectacle of a dream palace, her brush moving delicately over the fine rice paper; the mysterious penumbra of the pavilion that had sheltered her early passion, the vast halls crowded with amazing treasures, and above all, the first embrace of the only man whom she had ever really loved.

For a long while she remained thus, leaning against the side of the barge, bitterly reflecting upon the past.

Not daring to interrupt her meditations, her faithful attendants had shipped their oars and the barge, lightly rocked by a gentle breeze that wandered through the reeds, remained stationary.

Kneeling at Her Majesty's side, the Grand Eunuch Ngan-Te-Hai continued his mute and respectful orisons. He also felt his eyelids wet with tears; were not his regrets as cruel as hers!

146

He also dreamed of his youth and of his early ardours, but he had forfeited the right to express his sorrow and his pain could only appear supremely absurd.

A refined artist, he also expressed a deep distress at having beheld the destruction of such treasures of human imagination by the stupid vandalism of the Barbarians; but in his case, it was not only the destruction of the Summer Palace that he mourned, over and above all else he mourned his maimed virility. What could it profit him to be one of the richest and most powerful individuals in the Empire, since his grandeur only served to emphasise his pitiable condition! What would he not have given to be once more a man, were it only for an instant, and to appear as something other than a wretched impotent being in the eyes of his ideal mistress!

At that precise moment, Tseu-Hi looked at him with a profound gaze that betrayed all the perturbation of her lacerated heart. Wounded, she instinctively sought the appeasing caress as balm for her wound . . . what had he to offer her save the mystical embrace of his ardent spirit!

For a long time she gazed at him with strange insistence: he had indeed preserved a curious and infinitely appealing beauty.

He symbolised the ideal love that can never find realisation, and which, for that very reason, preserves a character both passionate and painful.

The Woman Who Commanded

And this woman who had suffered so grievously at the destruction of her bygone dreams experienced a mysterious attraction towards this martyr of love.

Bending over him, she murmured in a voice shaken by emotion:

"Give me at least the caress of your eyes! . . . I am in such dire need of love and consolation!"

But he lacked the courage even to raise his head: for he also was now weeping, and he felt desperately that the sight of his tears could only be ridiculous.

Meanwhile night was falling on the ruins of the Summer Palace. A great setting sun illumined them in all their sinister decay. Lurid reflections mirrored in the waters of the lake recalled the fires formerly kindled by the Barbarians. Nature appeared to bleed in unison with the heart of Tseu-Hi! Everywhere were patches as of blood upon the sombre mantle of night.

Rigid with emotion, the Empress drew herself erect upon the prow of her barge, and raising her arms to the glowing sky, poured forth her supplication to the heavens where dwelt the spirits of her glorious forebears!

She instinctively foresaw the impending end of the Dynasty, but before that consummation she intended to flash like a meteor across the universe.

Five Hundred Million Men

CHAPTER FIVE

In accordance with the advice volunteered by the astrologers after long deliberation, the funeral ceremony of the Emperor Hien-Foung was at length fixed to take place during the tenth moon. During four years, his brother the regent, Prince Kuong, had expended enormous sums upon the construction of the monument and upon preparations for the great event.

After a period of terrible trial, the Celestial Empire had recovered all its vitality and it was only seemly to celebrate this well-nigh miraculous resurrection.

It was therefore with unprecedented pomp that the miserable Hien-Foung was borne to his last resting-place by the members of that dynasty which he had brought to the very verge of ruin.

He who had been unable to maintain either order in his government, discipline in his army or any decent morale in his intimate circle, and who had ended by flying from the enemy in craven fear under the grotesque pretext of a tiger-hunt, was to receive the posthumous veneration of all those whom he had betrayed and deserted, and was duly to take his place among his glorious ancestors in full possession of his "Divine Dignity"! It should never be said in history that a Tsin had betrayed his blood or fallen short of his Godhead.

An entire people followed the heavy coffin to the distant sepulchre. First came the brothers of the deceased. the Princes Kuong and Tchouen and the two Empresses Tseu-Hi and Tseu-Ngan; after them walked all the other members of the imperial family, the ministers and high dignitaries and a mixed herd of priests, astrologers and other charlatans. These were again followed by eunuchs, mourning concubines and the numerous palace servants. The procession closed with an immense concourse of the humble faithful who crowded to perform this final pilgrimage.

On every side were musicians and keening women. Strings of rockets, designed to put to flight evil spirits, exploded incessantly, and the air hummed with the mournful murmur of ritual prayers punctuated by the deep pulsation of gongs and accompanied by the tolling of the Buddhist temple bells in the pagodas that lurked among the mist-shrouded plains.

Prancing at the head of his loyal Manchu cavalry rode the brilliant General Yong-Lou who had so successfully supplanted His deceased Majesty when yet alive! He was there in the post of honour earned by his loyal service.

It was in truth a prodigious spectacle to behold this endless procession making its solemn progress through the desolate and wintry land.

It was bent upon the exaltation of a god who

when on earth had never been anything but a clown: and yet this fact only served to increase their sense of importance!

Accustomed to all the melodrama of Autocracy, the Empress Tseu-Hi maintained an impressive calm.

Frozen into a hierarchical attitude in her palanquin, she passed like a venerated idol among the prostrated peasants who lined the road of the funeral procession. Was she not, always, in their eyes as in those of the populace of Peking, the "old buddha" whom a merciful providence had appointed to rule the Celestial Empire?

Only the day before, in her mysterious retreat at the Palace of Perpetual Spring, she had, in company with the Grand Eunuch and Yong-Lou, composed and executed a hymn of Supreme Rejoicing; but who could have suspicioned that fact on beholding her severe features and the heavy robes of deep mourning which she wore with such incomparable dignity?

In the eyes of the people she was the tragic widow, respectful of rites and tradition, who, in the gloomy retirement of the Forbidden City, would only tear herself from her sorrow in order to labour for the people's good. In such a manner do the masses learn respect for the Great of the Earth!

The Woman Who Commanded

CHAPTER SIX

For several uneventful years, the Empress Tseu-Hi continued to watch peacefully over the affairs of the Celestial Empire. Overflowing with youth and activity, she brought the selfsame ardour to the solemn exercise of authority in the bosom of the Grand Council, as to the enjoyment of her most joyous fantasies in the seclusion of the Palace of Perpetual Spring; moreover, she led this rather exacting dual existence without experiencing the slightest mental strain or a trace of physical exhaustion.

She was, in point of fact, not only the loveliest woman in China; she excelled all others in brain and physical endurance. One could but acknowledge her as a super-woman, an unique being such as only appears once in a thousand years.

No one ever even thought of disputing her incontestable supremacy: she seemed made by reason of her strength and her genius for world dominion. Untiring at work as in pleasure she was capable, with a smile on her lips, of outwearing a hundred ministers and a thousand lovers; she had a will of iron, nerves of steel and so prodigious a moral and physical resistance that a day's work or a night of debauch left her equally fresh and undismayed.

Five Hundred Million Men

Bravest of the brave, she had never feared anything or anyone, she had never allowed herself to be browbeaten either by the anger of men or the threats of nature.

But her greatest power had always dwelt in her limitless confidence in her own mind and body.

Dominating a world, she also knew the secret of self-mastery, and if she indulged in orgies of secret pleasure, it was always with edifying wisdom that she resumed her public rôle of Empress.

And yet it was an incredible fact that this virile sovereign had elected as her closest confidant an individual of minor importance who was not even a man. Wherein lay the strange attraction that linked this young and passionate woman to one who was the symbol of impotence!

It was, however, undeniable that the Grand Eunuch Ngan-Te-Hai was the only living soul who could boast of having retained some measure of influence over the proud and indomitable Tseu-Hi. Small wonder that he was half crazy with joy and arrogance or that the castrate became quite insufferable! Never stirring from his mistress' side, attending her behind the "lowered curtain" at the meetings of the Grand Council, just as he shared her banquets and perhaps her bed, he had become the spoilt lapdog, faithful but jealously distrustful, ready to bark at everyone and to bite all comers. Prince Kuong viewed him with particular dislike! Not only did he

justly consider him supremely offensive, but he also
regarded him as harmful to the State.

It was a fact that the favourite was no longer content with gratifying the desires and caprices of his
mistress; developing a singular ambition, he now
mixed slyly in public affairs with a view to increasing his personal importance and fortune. Knowing
that the Empress would never repudiate him, he soon
established in the Forbidden City a reign of terror
which quickly spread beyond its walls. Woe to anyone who had not the skill to gain his approval; touchy
in the extreme, he was tenaciously spiteful; the highest official was not sure of retaining his titles or even
his head unless he had contrived an entry into the
good graces of the Grand Eunuch.

Hidden in the shadows, listening at doors, spying
upon the merest gesture or the most trifling word, dis-
guising himself on occasion, the better to surprise his
adversaries, he established an all-pervading atmosphere of mysterious alarm.

The very members of the imperial family trembled
before his occult power; even in their own palaces,
behind closed and bolted doors, they were not perfectly at ease; they no longer dared to speak, they
hardly ventured to think, so well was it known that
the Grand Eunuch possessed a particularly alarming
faculty of divination. By means of striking examples
he had firmly implanted a general belief that he could
read the innermost hearts of men.

Five Hundred Million Men

Was he a wizard, or was he merely what we should now call a psychic? In any case he acquired knowledge of every conceivable secret. It was perhaps owing in part to this extraordinary gift that he retained the unqualified confidence of Tseu-Hi, who recognised in him not only the most devoted of servants but also the most invaluable of policemen.

There came a day, however, when Prince Kuong, literally worn out by the tyranny of the Grand Eunuch, resolved at any cost to rid the Court of this unscrupulous scoundrel. Having been for the hundredth time wounded in his dignity as premier prince imperial by this castrate of humble origin who now presumed to dictate to him as though he were the Son of Heaven Himself, he resolved to take immediate vengeance for this final affront. With this end in view he sought out his co-regent, the Empress Tseu-Ngan, in her Palace of the East, and begged her support in his perilous undertaking.

Tseu-Ngan who had lived peacefully in pleasant seclusion ever since the death of the Emperor Hien-Foung, being extremely careful not to meddle either in public affairs or in the most trivial intrigue, began by repudiating with horror the merest idea of being involved in such a conspiracy against the terrible Tseu-Hi. But Prince Kuong insisted, appealing both to her personal pride and to her well-known devotion to the Dynasty. He pointed out all the shame that History would heap upon the two of them if

155

they lacked the courage to shake off so ignoble a yoke, and he explained that the fate of the Celestial Empire itself was in hazard since it had come to depend upon the spiteful caprices of the Grand Eunuch.

Finally, by skilful allusions to a painful past and to the rivalry of the two women during the reign of Hien-Foung, he contrived to reopen wounds of self-esteem that had never very surely healed.

Briefly, by means of eloquence and persistence, he managed to convince Tseu-Ngan of the necessity for prompt action which would once and for all destroy the sinister influence which the favourite had acquired over Tseu-Hi; to this end there was only one possible means, which was also the best, and that was the suppression of the individual himself. Providentially, the Grand Eunuch had just left the Forbidden City on a visit to the province of Shan-Toung where Tseu-Hi had despatched him on a mission designed to raise supplementary taxes for the benefit of her private exchequer. It happened by a fortunate coincidence that Ting-Pao-Tchen, the governor of that province, was one of those few high functionaries who had retained a measure of independence and a remnant of courage under the autocracy of Tseu-Hi, and was not a mere puppet in her hands.

For personal reasons, he was moreover particularly devoted to Prince Kuong who, for his part, honoured him for the loyalty he had shown during the Taï-Ping rebellion. Despite the difference in their ranks, a deep affection united the two men who had mutually sworn a "brotherhood" in accordance with ancient Chinese tradition.

Prince Kuong could therefore count upon the passive obedience of Ting-Pao-Tchen to his Regent's commands, especially if they were strictly within the law. An ancient decree, promulgated at a time when the eunuchs possessed no power at Court and exercised no influence over the Son of Heaven, forbade these castrates under pain of death to leave the Forbidden City. It had been designed to avoid indiscretions that were always possible or intrigues with the outside world.

This law was well known to Prince Kuong and struck him as being singularly opportune for his purpose: he counted on its being carried out in its fullest sense by his "brother" Ting-Pao-Tchen.

It only remained to send the governor a decree to that effect. Obviously it would lack Tseu-Hi's signature, but that of Tseu-Ngan supporting the authority of Prince Kuong would suffice to convince a high official that he could legitimately put it into execution, since two out of three members of the Regency, that is to say a majority, had expressly commanded him to do so.

After a further and lengthy hesitation, Tseu-Ngan ended by making up her mind and affixed a trembling signature to this terrific decree; but she did not do so without cruel apprehensions as to the probable consequences to herself. "Who," she wailed, "will protect me from the fury of Tseu-Hi?" Already she regretted her action and besought Prince Kuong not to take advantage of her momentary weakness which had been unable to resist his urgency; but it was too late.

Prince Kuong, overjoyed at having succeeded by his flood of eloquence in obtaining from Tseu-Ngan a half unconscious signature, had lost no time in confiding the precious document to a special messenger who had been ordered to proceed with the utmost celerity to the governor of Shan-Toung. The precious opportunity was not likely to recur. Prince Kuong was achieving a veritable coup d'état and was under no delusions regarding the risks entailed.

But he was determined to risk everything, even death itself, rather than any longer endure the evil fatuity of the Grand Eunuch Ngan-Te-Hai.

Meanwhile, Tseu-Hi, who suspected nothing and who moreover would never have credited such an uprush of free-will on the part of Tseu-Ngan or such audacity on the part of Prince Kuong, was joyfully attending, in appropriate disguise, a grand nocturnal fête which she had organised together with her eunuchs and her women in the ancient gardens of the Forbidden City.

Never before had she taken so much pleasure in an entertainment; her only regret was owing to the temporary absence of her favourite, but was he not bent upon obtaining the money which would furnish other, yet more enjoyable, diversions! Ah, if she had only been able to foresee the consequences of that mission! But how could she conceive of such a horror? Who would ever dare so much as to question her potent authority, who would venture to oppose her most extravagant caprice?

She was omnipotent and her knowledge of the fact forbade any misgiving.

The Woman Who Commanded

CHAPTER SEVEN

Along the great imperial canal that leads to Pet-chili in Central China, Ngan-Te-Hai proceeded on his sumptuous journey. The mainmast of his junk displayed the imperial pennant, and the vessel itself was draped with banners adorned by the Dragon and the Phoenix, emblems of Supreme Power. Was he not indeed the special envoy of Her grandiose Majesty, the Empress Tseu-Hi, before whose authority five hundred million subjects bowed in reverence?

On the curved prow of the junk shone the two tra-ditional eyes, carved and painted in the wood and credited with power to perceive rocks ahead in time for the great fish to change its course, a provision which to Ngan-Te-Hai appeared ample for his com-plete security. What had he to fear from anyone, since he was protected by his imperial mission! He had disdainfully refused to accept so much as a single guard. The mere name of his Mistress would suffice to render his person as inviolable as that of a god.

On the other hand, a troupe of mummers cheered him on his journey, and, in the bows of the junk, fair musicians twanged stringed instruments while filling the air with the long-drawn notes of their shrill voices.

Five Hundred Million Men

Nonchalantly extended upon cushions of yellow silk, the Grand Eunuch smilingly volunteered little gestures of patronage to the numerous idlers who trotted along the banks escorting the wonderful junk and enjoying the spectacle afforded by so mighty an Excellency.

Naturally Ngan-Te-Hai, like any other self-respecting castrate, carried with him the jade receptacle which contained his "treasures" preserved in perfumed spirit.

For no one can foretell what may happen on a journey, and it is vitally important for a eunuch, should misfortune overtake him, to have his "treasures" beside him in his coffin.

In these circumstances, on arrival in another world, he may be certain of finding himself entire, once more on a sexual equality with those whom he may meet!

Moreover the jade receptacle, finely carved and adorned, evoked for Ngan-Te-Hai the happiest recollections. It was the Empress Tseu-Hi herself, who, as a delicate attention, had presented it to him on his birthday to replace a simpler receptacle which she had deemed unworthy.

For this reason, Ngan-Te-Hai, in an impulse of justifiable vanity, had placed beside him, on a mother-of-pearl pedestal, this remarkable work of art, which was thus exposed to the admiration of the other castrates. He felt a legitimate enjoyment of the envy that he thus aroused, which yet further enhanced his good humour.

The voyage had begun under the most favourable auspices and it promised to be extremely lucrative. The ambassador of Her Gracious Majesty Tseu-Hi had already succeeded in extorting a vast number of golden taels from various small functionaries, who had all but died of fright at the mere mention of his name! Now, nothing is more flattering than to be thus feared. It is the most pleasurable of popularities, particularly in the Far East.

Without an anxiety to cloud his serenity, Ngan-Te-Hai was congratulating himself upon being able to accomplish his journey in the full sunshine, which was a change from his nocturnal prowlings in the Forbidden City.

Inflated with arrogance he commanded his attendants to address him as: "Lord of Nine Thousand Years," in order to make it abundantly clear that in his own estimation at any rate he ranked only second to the Holy Man: "Lord of Ten Thousand Years"!

Suddenly, just at the moment when, drowsing in the pleasant warmth, he was sinking into beatific slumber, he was roused from his dreams by the abrupt halting of the junk.

The mainsail had come down with a run and a sharp jerk to the rudder had caused the vessel to tack in her own length and arrested her progress.

"What has happened?" cried the astonished Ngan-Te-Hai; but at that moment he perceived upon both banks of the canal, several hundred soldiers who, taking the place of the peaceable idlers, menaced the junk with levelled blunderbusses.

The musicians, the eunuchs and the flock of servants rent the air with panic-stricken cries, cowering in the hold like a swarm of rats at the appearance of a large cat. But Ngan-Te-Hai, drawing himself up with a certain swagger, addressed the general commanding these miscreants, inquiring indignantly:

"Have you by any chance taken leave of your senses? . . . Or can you possibly be ignorant of my identity? The imperial pennant and the Dragon and Phoenix banners should surely have sufficed to inform you."

But the general thus addressed replied dryly:

"All that is none of my business. I am simply here to carry out an order which I have received to intercept your progress."

"You do it with strange incivility," exclaimed the Grand Eunuch, "and you may have to pay dearly for your action. For I am Ngan-Te-Hai, the favourite of Her Omnipotent Majesty Tseu-Hi, who has deigned to send me on a mission, as you may ascertain from the document I bear which you will be good enough carefully to examine."

"That may be so," answered the imperturbable and discourteous warrior, "but I can only repeat that it is no affair of mine; moreover, I am entirely uneducated and incapable of deciphering any document that you might show me. The best course for you to follow is to come with me to His Excellency Ting-Pao-Tchen, governor of Shan-Toung, who impatiently awaits your arrival in his Yamen."

At these last words, Ngan-Te-Hai recovered all his composure. Obviously the governor, desirous of offering him his respectful salutations, accompanied by a weighty tithe, had despatched as emissary this idiotic general who had misunderstood the nature of his orders. Ngan-Te-Hai, therefore, announced in bantering tones:

"I have no desire to keep your Master waiting. I shall be happy to make his acquaintance and shall not fail to recommend you to him in glowing terms."

And giving the order to land, he quietly stepped on shore and joined the zealous general.

"Doubtless a palanquin awaits me, to which you will provide an escort?"

"Precisely!" replied the general, pointing to a superb litter which had been hidden from view behind the lines of soldiers.

Whereupon the Grand Eunuch, having directed his suite quietly to await his return, stepped cheerfully into the litter in order to seek His Excellency the Governor.

But he was inwardly quite determined, so soon as the customary compliments should have been exchanged, to inform His Excellency of his subordinate's blunder and to see that worthy's head fall to the ground.

After several hours of travelling, Ngan-Te-Hai arrived without incident before the walls of the town in which was situated the Yamen of Ting-Pao-Tchen. The bearers, still surrounded by a valiant escort, passed through the great gates of the city and then along tortuous streets crowded with curious folk who pressed forward to see the grand personage.

The entrance to the Yamen was masked by a screening wall upon which the conventional tiger was painted in garish colours.

Suspecting nothing, Ngan-Te-Hai, having left the litter and passed round this wall, entered the court of honour of the Yamen through an entrance guarded on either side by two great red lacquer war-gods. A host of servants immediately sent up the customary salute of welcoming rockets, while upon the threshold of the principal pavilion the Governor Ting-Pao-Tchen, in full regalia, greeted the august visitor from afar with noble gestures of his closed fists.

Ngan-Te-Hai who, for all his customary arrogance, was not averse from showing that he was not ignorant of polite usages, correctly returned gesture for gesture; he then gravely accompanied the Governor into the interior of the Hall of Honour where he took his seat in the magnificent chair prepared for his accommodation.

The Woman Who Commanded

As was customary, a number of servants soon appeared, bringing fine porcelain bowls of tea, saucers of water-melon seeds and hookahs. Having deposited their burdens upon a table placed at the visitor's elbow, they discreetly withdrew, and Ting-Pao-Tchen gravely opened the conversation:

"It is for me a most signal honour thus to receive in my Yamen so illustrious a personage!"

This compliment was solemnly succeeded by a few more fine phrases.

Ngan-Te-Hai listened inattentively to these traditional words and in his opinion extremely tedious flatteries. Having rather briefly replied to them, he inquired bluntly:

"I should be grateful if Your Excellency would be so good as to explain to me without further delay the motive of this meeting."

"I am entirely at your command," answered Ting-Pao-Tchen politely, and drawing from the wide sleeve of his robe the imperial decree which bore the signatures of Prince Kuong and the Empress Tseu-Ngan, he slowly started to read it aloud.

Ngan-Te-Hai listened in stunned amazement, asking himself what could be the meaning of this abominable mystery. Meanwhile Ting-Pao-Tchen, with a final deep obeisance, announced:

"It now only remains, Lord of Nine Thousand Years, for me to have you officially beheaded in the

courtyard of my Yamen with all the ceremony due to
your exalted rank."

At these words Ngan-Te-Hai grew very pale. He
began to protest:

"I have been sent into this province by the all-
powerful Empress Tseu-Hi. I have loyally obeyed
her orders and have done nothing for which I could
be held to blame."

The Governor made an evasive gesture.

"I am sorry, but the decree regarding you is im-
perative; it even states definitely that I am to lend
no ear to your explanations, however ingenious or
honest they may appear to be. I am commanded
promptly and rigorously to fulfil the law which con-
demns to death any eunuch who has left the walls of
the Forbidden City."

Ngan-Te-Hai retorted with growing agitation:

"But I repeat that it is by the express command
of Her Majesty the Empress Tseu-Hi that I have
quitted the Forbidden City; the law therefore becomes null and void. . . . Moreover, what is this
law? I, for my part, have never heard of it."

The Governor answered coldly:

"Their Highnesses Prince Kuong and the Empress
Tseu-Ngan have commanded me to pay no heed to
your recriminations. Will you therefore kindly regard me from now on as completely deaf to any kind
of eloquence?"

The Woman Who Commanded

Whereupon he signed to an officer of the guard who watched by the door, saying:

"I place His Excellency in your hands. You know what remains to be done."

Having thus spoken, Ting-Pao-Tchen with chill courtesy put his lips to the bowl of tea that stood before him, thus signifying that the interview was at an end; after which, rising deliberately from his chair, he gravely bowed to the Grand Eunuch and made a dignified exit.

Meanwhile, Ngan-Te-Hai, after remaining for some moments prostrate in his handsome chair, suddenly sprang to his feet, crying:

"This miserable governor has taken leave of his senses! Let no one dare to heed his orders! I am Ngan-Te-Hai, the Grand Eunuch of the Forbidden City, I am the favourite of Her Omnipotent Majesty the Empress Tseu-Hi, I am myself the Lord of Nine Thousand Years! . . . Woe to anyone who affronts such authority!"

But already soldiers had been summoned who were brutally hustling him towards the centre of the Court of Honour. With a blow in the ribs they forced him to his knees and bound his hands behind his back. Ngan-Te-Hai, who felt as though in a nightmare, was by now wailing.

"But all this is impossible! . . . Am I the prey of a horrible hallucination?"

And all around him the soldiers sniggered:

Five Hundred Million Men

"He is crazy with terror!"

Then the poor wretch, wounded in his dignity, fought to recover a measure of self-control in order not to meet death too cravenly among these boors.

Before his haggard eyes arose the adorable image of his divine Mistress. Once more he seemed to see her beautiful form extended upon the silken cushions as she awaited in her innocent timidity his strange examination. What a dagger it had been in his heart to behold this new and admirable concubine! Then, abruptly, it was the indomitable Sovereign who appeared to him at Jehol, her proud visage transfigured by ambition. Finally it was the Empress Tseu-Hi herself, so generously admitting him to her confidence, so graciously and lovingly smiling upon his devotion!

And he must perish here, idiotically, without even being able to tell her once more how desperately he had loved her to the end! Already the Grand Executioner had arrived and was cheerfully sharpening his sword on a polished stone. His assistant approached the victim and seizing his long pigtail, drew the head well forward so that the neck should be extended horizontally. Grasping his sword in both hands, the Grand Executioner raised it, bounding into the air with a shrill cry of: "Hé! . . ."

"Han!" he concluded on a deeper note as he regained his feet while the sword blade, describing a flashing arc, fell swift and true upon the nape of the victim's neck. The bloodless head rolled to the ground, while from the still kneeling body the ghastly wound poured forth a horrible fountain of hot blood. With a contemptuous kick the Grand Executioner sent the head to rejoin the body which had now collapsed, remarking callously:

"They ought not to be separated. Ngan-Te-Hai will already be sufficiently embarrassed at having to present himself at the Yellow Fountains without his 'treasures' which must have remained on board of his junk."

But the Governor Ting-Pao-Tchen, arriving on the scene, gave orders that messengers should be sent in haste to fetch the jade receptacle, the elegant gift made to her faithful confidant by the Empress Tseu-Hi.

Moreover, he made it his personal care that both the head and the "treasures" should be properly placed beside the mutilated body in the magnificent coffin which he provided for his august visitor. He was an honourable man who wished to keep his word and fulfil his courteous promise to send Ngan-Te-Hai to the Yellow Fountains with all the attentions due to his rank as Grand Eunuch.

Five Hundred Million Men

CHAPTER EIGHT

When Tseu-Hi learnt of the shameful end of the Grand Eunuch Ngan-Te-Hai, she experienced a moment of sheer stupor: they had actually dared, against all conceivable expectation, to assassinate her favourite under the pretext of an obsolete law, and what was still more serious, they had not feared to defy her all-powerful authority!

Wounded both in her imperial dignity and in her womanly affection, Tseu-Hi swore there and then to accept the challenge to her power and to avenge her friend. She immediately sent for her faithful Yong-Lou, and, having in a few words explained to him her righteous grievance, she demanded his support and succour. Since her adversaries had not hesitated to make treacherous use of violence, she would in her turn employ force, but frankly, in the open day.

In the twinkling of an eye the entire Manchu Guard was mobilised and the palaces of the Empress Tseu-Ngan and of Prince Kuong surrounded by a triple cordon of warriors devoted to the death to their "old buddha"!

At which juncture, Tseu-Hi, terrible to behold, marched into the Palace of the East and indignantly upbraided her co-regent:

The Woman Who Commanded

"Well, Madam! And do you for one instant cherish the illusion that your presumption will remain unpunished? . . . You have actually dared, without consulting me, to append your signature to that disgraceful decree that was sent to the governor of Shan-Toung commanding him to suppress the Grand Eunuch Ngan-Te-Hai, whom I had formally entrusted with a mission in that province! . . . Now listen to me, and make no mistake as to the fact that you will not be allowed any further opportunity of perfidiously abusing the power with which I was foolish enough to invest you. . . . From this day onwards you cease to exist in the government. Not only do I forbid your attending the meetings of the Grand Council, but I shall also prevent you from ever leaving this palace upon any pretext whatsoever! . . . Furthermore, you will be good enough to accept the constant society of a dozen of my loyal eunuchs who will throughout each day and night observe and report to me your words and actions. . . . As you may see, I shun your methods, I am perfectly frank and do not care to dissemble . . . I am hurling my rage and my contempt straight in your face and reasons of State alone, which constrain me to avoid scandal, prevent me from delivering you over, here and now, to the punishment you have so richly deserved. . . . But you will lose nothing by the delay!"

She ceased and with a contemptuous gesture she made as though to strike the Empress of the East.

Tseu-Ngan, appalled, wailed: "I had a moment of aberration! I confess it and most humbly beg your forgiveness. But I only yielded to the insistence of Prince Kuong."

Tseu-Hi shrugged her shoulders disdainfully:

"Having committed the crime, you lack even the courage to admit your responsibility, and foolishly try to heap upon another the burden of your own baseness. Such behaviour, far from mollifying me, only adds to the disgust with which I already viewed your character."

Having thus spoken, she turned on her heel and departed abruptly, banging the doors of the Palace of the East.

Still highly perturbed, she proceeded to Prince Kuong's residence and burst in upon him without even the formality of announcement.

He, in his turn, was violently brought to book.

"Will you also, I wonder, have the impudence," cried she defiantly, "to deny your crime in order to escape from its consequences?"

Her speech was accompanied from without by the suggestive clash of swords.

Stung to the quick by the insult, he sprang to his feet, proudly folding his arms:

"It is not my habit, Madam, to shirk my responsibilities. Certainly I ordered Ting-Pao-Tchen to behead the Grand Eunuch Ngan-Te-Hai, whose influence over Your Majesty seemed to me detrimental to the vital interests of the Celestial Empire and contrary to the honour of the Dynasty and of our House. I only signed the document commanding his execution in full knowledge of all relevant circumstances and after mature consideration of the possible consequences. I was perfectly aware that by so doing I exposed myself to this outburst of fury, which I fully expected and which, consequently, does not take me by surprise."

Tseu-Hi suggested satirically:

"Why not go a step further and admit that you perpetrated this outrage, not simply and solely for reasons of State, but chiefly in order to avenge your own wounded pride?"

"Precisely, Madam, that was also my motive, for I was not prepared to allow a castrate to assume precedence over the Son of the Emperor Tao-Kouang. . . . While I can have no illusions regarding the doom that awaits me, I shall still answer you truthfully and without evasion: I have no regrets for what I have done and should, if necessary, repeat my action!"

"What effrontery!" exclaimed Tseu-Hi.

"No, Madam," replied Prince Kuong. "It is merely that I am conscious of the dignity of my rank and of the importance of my position. My last desire is to die an honest man; the Premier Prince of the Celestial Empire must at least be worthy of his blood! . . . You can do with me exactly as you please, your decision will find me completely indifferent, for I feel that to the very last I have done my duty."

A great silence followed this unexpected oration.

The generous nature of Tseu-Hi held courage in such high esteem that she could not but admire it even in her worst enemy.

Looking the Regent straight in the eyes, she addressed him:

"Prince Kuong, your behaviour toward me has been inexcusable, but I am forced to admit that your courage has never been wanting. Long ago, you gave noble evidence of your contempt of danger when you remained at your post when the Violet Town was surrounded by the Barbarians, and since then you have always evinced a virile energy in the most difficult situations, not only in opposing those conspirators who attempted to usurp authority but also in the final repression of the Taï-Ping rebellion. Even now, you have the courage to brave my displeasure which is no trifling matter in view of the crime which you have ventured to commit and for which I have both the justification and the means whereby to exact immediate expiation. . . . For these reasons I see myself reluctantly compelled, as Empress Dowager, to consider the interests of the Dynasty and to confirm you in your authority as Regent; you will therefore, as in the past, continue to support me at the sittings of the Grand Council and I shall leave in your hands the direction of public affairs. . . . You will realise that I also am capable of placing the State before any other consideration. . . . But as a woman, Prince Kuong, I swear that I will never forgive you, and I frankly warn you that the woman you so unworthily baffled will remain your bitter enemy; the day will come when she can take vengeance, and she will not spare you."

Bowing stiffly to the astonished Regent, she went to seek Yong-Lou who, with his troops, was waiting to arrest Prince Kuong.

Without evasion she admitted:

"I have reflected; my hatred of Prince Kuong remains unaltered, but I regard his authority as indispensable to the welfare of the State. He will therefore remain Regent as in the past, and you must pay him respect and obedience."

Then she sighed:

"There are times when it is very bitter to be an Empress!"

Having returned to her Palace of Perpetual Spring, she summoned her household and announced with solemnity:

"The Grand Eunuch is dead! . . . Long live the Grand Eunuch!"

And she straightway appointed as successor to the unfortunate Ngan-Te-Hai the young Li-Lien-Yn,[1]

[1] Familiarly known among the populace as Li-Pi-Siao.

who was his equal in beauty and intelligence. Over-whelmed, the castrate flung himself at the feet of the Empress to thank her for her signal favour and to swear a boundless devotion. But Tseu-Hi promptly raised him, saying in kindly accents:

"I hope that I shall never have cause to regret my choice and that you will know how to please, to amuse and to instruct me."

And she looked at him with so singular an ex-pression that Li-Lien-Yn felt some misgivings; he had begun to realise that it might be no easy task adequately to replace the favourite.

The Woman Who Commanded

At the end of that year (1872) the Holy Man Toung-Tche entered the seventeenth year of his age. This event brought the Regency to a close and the Empress Dowager, in compliance with immemorial custom, was obliged to render up the Supreme Authority into the hands of her legally adult son.

Obviously Tseu-Hi could not hope to avoid this sacred obligation, but it was with real regret, mingled with anxiety, that she beheld Toung-Tche actively ascend the Dragon's Throne.

She had come to realise, through practical experience, the weight of the task which devolved upon so young a man! How could he possibly possess the wisdom and judgment requisite for maintaining order and peace in so vast a country as China,—a China, moreover, still suffering the reaction from the terrible civil disturbances that had ravaged it during the reign of the preceding emperor, Hien-Foung?

Even granting him the most signal qualities, would he not suffer cruelly from lack of experience?

And all that work of reconstructing the vastest Empire of the universe, of which Tseu-Hi had been so proud, might it not now be compromised, if not destroyed for ever? The whole country, together with the Dynasty, might once more be called to endure those terrible hours when the victorious yells of the Barbarians would mingle with incitements to rebellion, to pillage and to murder vociferated by revolutionaries and conspirators. How was a recurrence of such disaster to be avoided?

Undoubtedly Tseu-Hi hoped to retain a measure of influence over her son, but would it always suffice to avert danger from the throne?

It was so frequently necessary to act suddenly and with determined energy! What would happen when Tseu-Hi would only be in a position to counsel a needful act of authority and would no longer have the right to perform it?

Finally, it seemed both unjust and humiliating to this remarkable sovereign who had held the power with such mastery and genius, to find herself suddenly relegated to a back seat, contrary to her instincts of pride and patriotism.

Nevertheless, Tseu-Hi, putting a good face upon a bad business and never despairing of final success, resolved in any case to hold as many trumps as possible in the new game in which she was driven to take a hand.

She began by marrying the Holy Man to a daughter of the Imperial Tutor, a girl named Ha-Lou-To, who would, she believed, remain her tool. She not unnaturally thought that the new Empress, recognising that she owed her elevation entirely to her mother-in-law, would remain that latter's obedient and grateful servant, and serve her, at need, as a useful ally against Toung-Tche.

In any case, the Empress Consort would furnish timely reports to the Empress Dowager regarding the more or less private designs of the Holy Man; these would serve as a guide to action and were not to be despised.

Unhappily for Tseu-Hi, the young imperial couple, becoming devotedly attached against all expectations, promptly began to demonstrate a most regrettable spirit of independence. Toung-Tche, who had inherited from Tseu-Hi a certain arrogance of character, appeared by no means reconciled to remaining in leading-strings. He displayed the clearest intentions of exerting his own high authority without deferring to any influence, not even that of his venerable mother.

And Tseu-Hi perceived with consternation that the ungrateful Ha-Lou-To, far from remaining her tool, had gone over enthusiastically to her husband's side in each and every dispute that arose between the Holy Man and the erstwhile Regent.

Tseu-Hi was, of course, far too intelligent openly to show her displeasure at the conduct of her son and his wife. Advertising, on the contrary, a feigned indifference for matters connected with the Sovereign Authority which she appeared to have definitely renounced, she made every effort to conciliate the young married couple in order to be constantly in their society and to lose no opportunity, should one arise, of fomenting dissension between them.

Skilfully flattering the youthful pride of the Holy Man, she gradually succeeded in associating herself so completely with his daily life that he soon began to follow the perfidious counsels given him by his venerable mother with regard to pleasurable indulgences. The ground was well-prepared in this respect, for if Toung-Tche resembled his mother in his energetic enthusiasm both at work and at play, he had, on the other hand, inherited from his father Hien-Foung an alarming predilection for liquor, debauch and every description of vice.

Instead of maternally restraining these unworthy instincts, Tseu-Hi set herself with fiendish ingenuity to the employment of every possible means that would favour their development, and, aided in this evil task by her new favourite, the Grand Eunuch Li-Lien-Yn, she was not long in transforming the Emperor Toung-Tche into an excellent imitation of his pitiable predecessor.

With incredible amorality, Tseu-Hi became the confidante of the Holy Man, encouraging his grievances when he complained bitterly of the Tribunal of Rites and the Court of Censors which did not cease from reproving him or from severely reminding him of his moral obligations and of the thousand and one rules of a complicated etiquette.

The Woman Who Commanded

"Ah, venerable mother," sighed the Holy Man one day, "I can neither make a gesture nor say a word that is not registered and discussed by unpleasant old men who poison my existence by their offensive presence. I have not the right to dress as I choose nor to eat what I fancy, nor to select my own companions, even in bed. An unceasing tyranny oppresses my youth, and I have not one moment of genuine freedom. I am scarcely permitted to sneeze or to blow my nose without seeing a record made of that astounding event. . . . In short, I am sick to death of being a slave to my grandeur, and I have come to envy the humblest of my subjects who can follow the dictates of his heart, or at any rate, sleep alone should he be so inclined."

"Do not let it trouble you," replied Tseu-Hi in accents of hypocritical gentleness. "I will do everything I can to dispel your tedium and to render your position less painful, and I shall be only too happy if I can succeed."

Whereupon, she summoned the Grand Eunuch Li-Lien-Yn, who, after respectfully flinging himself at the feet of the Holy Man, offered to employ every means in his power to assist him to cast off the official yoke.

They agreed together that they would disguise themselves that very evening in order to seek distraction outside the tedious precincts of the Forbidden City.

Five Hundred Million Men

Li-Lien-Yn undertook that one of the gates should be guarded by castrates so loyal and so discreet that the imperial escapade would remain a profound secret, and that once outside, he would know how to conduct His Majesty to places of enjoyment of which he had never so much as heard tell, and which would be likely to rouse him from his deadly boredom.

With all the enthusiasm of his seventeen years, the Son of Heaven seized upon the project of an adventure which would so happily vary the monotony of his official life. Twilight having fallen, he assumed the robes of a well-to-do plebeian sent to him by Li-Lien-Yn, and skilfully painted his imperial countenance in such a fashion as to alter it beyond recognition. Then, delightfully perturbed, he slipped out into the mauve shadows which filled the courts of the Violet Town, in order to seek the Grand Eunuch in a corner of the ancient park. Having walked together in silence for some time in order to avoid attracting the attention of the sentinels, a precaution which caused His Majesty much amusement, the two conspirators reached a small concealed door, watched on this occasion, for greater security, by a few deaf and dumb castrates who owed a deathless devotion to their Lord and to the Grand Eunuch.

Very soon, Toung-Tche had passed unchallenged through the outer defences of the Forbidden City; he was actually outside, alone and as free as air: it was almost more than a Holy Man could believe!

The Woman Who Commanded

A high two-wheeled cart with a blue hood, such as are frequently seen in the streets of Peking, was awaiting the arrival of the night-birds. The sycophant who was to drive the vehicle was also a deaf-mute castrate entirely devoted to the Grand Eunuch and, moreover, ignorant as to the identity of his master's companion.

At a sign from Li-Lien-Yn, the cart drew near. The Holy Man and the Grand Eunuch climbed quickly into it and concealed themselves under the discreet shadows of the hood.

The handsome mule harnessed to the equipage was off at a touch of the reins, trotting briskly toward one of the straight, wide avenues which traverse the Tartar Town from north to south. Having passed through the great gate in the ramparts, the vehicle turned into the circuitous byways of the Chinese quarter. These were a scene of joyous animation. Thousands of lanterns threw multicoloured rays upon the open air shops and the little street stalls. Great panels of lacquered wood bearing commercial signs in golden characters on a scarlet ground, swung in the breeze above the heads of the pedestrians.

The crowd was dense and noisy. In the chairs that passed swiftly, borne by hurrying bearers, ancient Excellencies bent upon illicit pleasures nodded their hoary heads, while other litters concealed lovely dancers who smiled behind transparent curtains as they were carried to the tea houses.

Five Hundred Million Men

With intense curiosity, Toung-Tche peered from beneath the blue hood: the Holy Man, condemned always to remain cloistered within his temple, gazed rapturously at the spectacle of real life.

Never had he beheld any aspect of the outside world save the great solemn main arteries of the capital, cleared by military command and guarded on those occasions when he went to offer the traditional prayers at the Temple of Heaven or to turn the first furrow of the year in the symbolic field of the Temple of Agriculture; and now, beneath his eyes fermented the lively seething crowd of his subjects in a natural and cheerful setting. A contrast indeed!

He had never before seen more than the gloomy faces of court officials who looked as though carved in wood, so completely were they petrified into their conventional attitudes, and he had heard only conventional phrases and stale discourses, and the tedious reading of uninteresting imperial decrees which were reputed to be of his unaided composition.

What an intense relief to escape for a few moments from that mouldy grandiose atmosphere which positively exuded boredom, and to hear the common herd of mortals proclaiming their joy of living in ordinary everyday language and see them frolic thoughtlessly without the slightest constraint upon the thresholds of popular restaurants, alehouses and brothels.

The Holy Man was in ecstasy, although still faintly fearful that he might be recognised during this questionable adventure. But the Grand Eunuch hastened to reassure him: to begin with, His August Majesty was so effectually disguised that no one, even of his daily intimacy, could possibly suspect his identity; moreover, his subjects were entirely unfamiliar with his features since upon those rare occasions when he passed through the capital they were relegated to a seemly distance and constrained to respectful prostration; finally, who could be expected to have such overweening presumption as to suppose that the Son of Heaven would issue forth at night from his inviolable sanctuary for a spree among the vilest of his subjects?

Having succeeded in persuading the Holy Man that he ran no risk in descending from his vehicle, Li-Lien-Yn finally enticed him into a celebrated brothel where it was pleasantly possible to indulge every species of vice, from common drunkenness to the delicate stupor of opium, halting at every stage of amorous phantasy that the age or means of the client would permit.

The first room which they entered served as a relatively seemly antechamber to the private apartments. In it were seated numerous clients before small square tables, drinking tea, nibbling watermelon seeds or solemnly smoking white metal hookahs engraved with licentious scenes. In the middle of the room was a raised platform upon which young and attractive Chinese dancers with little broken feet,

uttered shrill warblings to a concealed accompaniment
of flutes and violins. Slipping quietly through the
crowd the Holy Man and the Grand Eunuch established themselves in a corner where they sought at
first to avoid attracting attention; but very soon
Toung-Tche was unable to resist casting covetous
glances at the celebrated tiny feet in which, according to age-old tradition, lay a woman's centre of
modesty.

These "golden lilies" were a change from the Empress Consort and from his concubines who, being
Manchus, had natural feet, and he eagerly desired
to examine these novelties more closely.

Perceiving the interest aroused in the new client
by the "golden lilies," the proprietor came forward
to inquire his pleasure which he expressed himself
as willing immediately to gratify. He entered into
a laudatory description of the delights which his
renowned establishment could offer its patrons.

"The passage at the far end of this hall," he
explained, "leads to a number of well-furnished apartments where one can revel in perfect security among
agreeable society. Our cooking is superfine, as are
also our women. . . . There is an endless variety of
dishes available to suit all purses, ranging from
pigeons' eggs poached on bamboo hearts to sea-cater-
pillars with long black fins soused in garlic; there are
also females of all ages from little shy-eyed virgins
to matrons of the maturest experience. . . . Finally,

if Your Excellencies have other ends in view, you can descend by this stairway that is almost at your elbows to luxurious cellars where, far from all noise, in an enticing twilight, are rows of comfortable couches inviting the opīum-smoker . . . the mats are of the finest, the pillows exquisitely clean, the drug of superlative quality and the little boys who prepare the pipes are as well trained as they are undeniably attractive. . . ."

The worthy proprietor was babbling on without intermission in the hopes of rousing his honourable clients to some profitable desire, when the Holy Man, pulling the Grand Eunuch by the sleeve, whispered in his ear:

"Would it not be pleasant to begin by a lively supper before seeking the cellars?"

"Your Majesty is well inspired," replied Li-Lien-Yn in an undertone. Greed was indeed his besetting sin, being the only vice which he was still in a position to enjoy.

They made their way to a small private room, where they were promptly joined, at the Holy Man's request, by several broken-footed dancers.

This seemed an innocent enough beginning, and yet it was with considerable difficulty when the Hour of the Tiger drew near, that the Holy Man, supported by the sympathetic Grand Eunuch, contrived to climb into the mule-cart which trotted smartly off on its return journey to the Forbidden City.

Five Hundred Million Men

At dawn, when the Son of Heaven came to occupy the Dragon's Throne as President of the Meeting of the Grand Council, his uncles, the Princes Kuong and Tchouen, remarked with consternation the growing resemblance of Toung-Tche to his august father, the late Emperor Hien-Foung. They noted the early development of all the stigmata from the dissipated eyes to the alcoholic complexion.

But as she sat behind the "lowered curtain," the Empress Dowager listened complacently while Li-Lien-Yn, who stood at her side, viewing the proceedings through the slits in the fabric, informed her of the amazing condition of her divine son, Toung-Tche.

Already she possessed the comfortable certainty of quickly resuming the sovereign power.

The Woman Who Commanded

CHAPTER TEN

There came a morning when the Dragon's Throne was vacant. The Holy Man, like a truant schoolboy, had not only slept out, but he had not returned for the hour of duty.

The members of the Grand Council cancelled the meeting in horrified silence, while Tseu-Hi, brisk and delighted, further emphasised her son's misdoings by hypocritical inquiries as to his whereabouts.

The sun was already high in the heavens when Li-Lien-Yn and his deaf and dumb assistants bore back to the Imperial Palace a human parcel chastely draped with a yellow silk veil. The parcel in question was His Majesty the Emperor Toung-Tche, dead drunk.

Three more times during the same moon was this ghastly scandal repeated; for Toung-Tche, having once relaxed the curb upon his vices, lost all control over himself. Insatiable, ever in search of a new sensation more unwholesome than its predecessors, he nightly hurried from den to den of the Chinese Quarter, accompanied by the lowest characters and the most degraded prostitutes of both sexes.

His rioting ceased only when exhaustion supervened or when a final cup of spirit felled him in an unconscious heap upon some filthy bed in a house of ill-fame.

It was then that the Grand Eunuch, who was careful to remain sober, would pay the bill and place the inert form of His Majesty in the customary cart which would take him back to the Forbidden City. But it was no easy task in full daylight, even with the strictest precautions, to smuggle such merchandise into the Violet Town without arousing suspicions.

In the Household of the Son of Heaven rumours began to circulate and very soon there remained no minister or high official who was unaware of the pitiable moral and physical degeneration of His Majesty, whose health had suffered as much as his reputation.

At which juncture, Tseu-Hi, without officially resuming the supreme authority, allowed it to be understood in a few vigorous sentences, followed by immediate active confirmation, that she had once more become the erstwhile all-powerful sovereign who was determined to conduct matters according to her lights. And without argument, thankful indeed at recovering an authority essential to the salvation of the Dynasty and to the good of the Celestial Empire, all the members of the imperial family together with the various high officials submitted themselves once more obediently to the rule of the Dowager-Empress.

Only the Empress Consort, Ha-Lou-To haughtily

protested against this usurpation of power and strenu-
ously opposed her terrible mother-in-law.

Violent scenes broke out between the two women,
Tseu-Hi bitterly reproaching her daughter-in-law
for revolting ingratitude, while Ha-Lou-To retaliated
by accusing the shameless mother of having encouraged her son in debauchery in order to supplant him
on the Dragon's Throne.

Finally, one evening, after an unusually sharp dispute, Ha-Lou-To imprudently exclaimed:

"If the time should come when the Holy Man,
who has lately seemed very unwell, should ascend
the Dragon's Chariot and go to rejoin his glorious
ancestors at the Yellow Fountains, it will be upon
me, Madam, and not upon you that the Regency will
devolve, for I shall in my turn have become Empress
Mother and shall be quite capable of asserting my
rights and those of the heir whom I shall have given
to the Throne."

And she pointed with a proud finger to her womb,
which already bore imperial fruit.

Speechless for a moment at such daring, Tseu-Hi
none the less reflected before replying ominously:

"You would be well advised to hasten your confinement, Madam, and the realisation of your high ambitions."

And disdainfully putting an end to the interview,
she shrugged her shoulders and moved away.

In her innermost heart she was thinking that Ha-

Lou-To had very imprudently signed her own death warrant, and that she might have acted more wisely and effectually had she taken subtler means to attain her ends.

"She is nothing but a little fool, after all, inflated by puerile vanity," concluded Tseu-Hi with a savage smile; "she can easily bear her husband company upon the long journey, for I shall know how to facilitate her departure."

Soothed by this pleasant reflection, she joined Li-Lien-Yn who was awaiting her at the Palace of Perpetual Spring.

She rapidly informed her confidant of her daughter-in-law's insulting behaviour, and begged him to keep his castrates well in hand so that they might at any moment support her should she be suddenly compelled to accomplish some sort of coup d'état.

She then sent for her faithful Yong-Lou and informed him fully of the situation, asking him also to hold himself and his guards in readiness to intervene, should it prove necessary in her favour.

Finally she commanded Li-Houng-Tchang, to whom she had given the governorship of Petchili in recompense for his good services against the Taï-Ping, that he was secretly to mobilise his entire army which might very shortly be called into action.

Having thus taken all due precautions against the possibility of a desperate struggle, Tseu-Hi went to bed in the most peaceful frame of mind imaginable, while her divine son, more abandoned than ever, instead of decently receiving one of his concubines in the Chamber of the Sacred Repose, slunk guiltily out to the Chinese Quarter in search of new and unseemly adventures.

Five Hundred Million Men

Word had gone forth throughout the Violet Town that the Holy Man had had the good fortune to blossom; a phrase which translated into vulgar terms signified that he was covered with pustules. The fact was that in the course of his career through a succession of filthy brothels he had contrived to contract that black smallpox which, in the Far East, is as common as it is terrible.

Immediately the entire Court, not excluding those personally attending His Majesty, began to estimate the probabilities as to who would succeed him in the event of his death.

Ha-Lou-To, the Empress Consort, had not completed the term of her pregnancy and she might, moreover, be delivered of a girl child, which event would leave the succession open to a number of aspirants.

With that gambling instinct which has always been a Manchu as well as a Chinese characteristic, every high official began to bet upon one or another widely divergent prospect. Some felt that Tseu-Hi would contrive with her indomitable energy to hang on to the Power; others counted on the event of Ha-Lou-To having the good fortune to bear a son; others

195

again preferred the claims of one or another prince of the imperial family, any of whom was entitled, for one or another reason, to put forward a son as candidate for the imperial succession, on one or another more or less valid ground.

Briefly, the Forbidden City became once again a nest of intrigue such as it had been at the time of the death of Hien-Foung, and rival clans formed underhand alliances, and expended their strength in futile bickering.

Thanks to the fact that her enemies were divided amongst themselves and to their consequent indiscretions, Tseu-Hi had little difficulty in remaining fully informed regarding their projects and their ambitions.

Li-Lien-Yn, who had honourably succeeded his illustrious predecessor, the late lamented Ngan-Te-Hai, in the functions of imperial spy, afforded his royal mistress the loyal support of his consummate rascality.

Always on the watch, hiding behind a screen or listening at doors, skilfully insinuating himself under a disguise into the various opposing factions, he contrived to gain information of the deepest designs of his most suspicious enemies, which was promptly reported to the Empress Mother who was shrewd enough to appear completely ignorant of the intrigues that were being woven around her.

Resolved to strike suddenly and decisively, she was not likely to commit the error of awakening the

suspicions of her prospective victims. She therefore remained impenetrable, feigning to concentrate
all her activity and ingenuity exclusively upon the
wise direction of the State; she certainly made hourly
inquiries regarding the health of her son, but was
she not actually constrained to do so by every precedent?

In point of fact she wished to be the first to learn
of the Holy Man's decease so that she might equally
be the first to take action; a worthy descendant of
Manchu warriors, her taste was for offensives and
for sudden attacks that surprise and demoralise the
enemy.

As for weeping crocodile tears over the imminent
dissolution of Toung-Tche, she regarded such a
demonstration as perfectly futile and opposed to her
dignity and true sentiments. She had never nourished
the slightest affection for this son of Hien-Foung
who, in reminding her of his father, recalled for her
the most humiliating and the most unpleasant experiences of her entire life.

She had never taken the smallest interest in him,
and had left to her co-regent, the Empress Tseu-
Ngan, the entire care of his rearing and education.

Undoubtedly Toung-Tche during his minority had
for his mother represented a cardinal interest as being
the trump card in her claims to personal power, but
since his coming of age he had ceased in the eyes
of the omnipotent Empress to be anything but an

opponent to her authority, who, moreover, stood for a future reign which she correctly foresaw as disadvantageous to the Empire.

Tseu-Hi, therefore, felt no regret at the thought that Toung-Tche was preparing to rejoin his father at the Yellow Fountains; on the contrary, she regarded this imminent departure as favourable to her personal ambitions and indispensable to the prosperity of the State. However, she had, as was seemly, summoned to her son's bedside all the most celebrated physicians in the Celestial Empire.

These experts, compelled by ritual to remain incessantly prostrated before their august client, and having therefore no opportunity of even perceiving his countenance, were none the less, after a prudent consultation to ensure unanimity, able to furnish a learned diagnosis of his condition, couched in nebulous and involved terms and thickly studded with expressions of the profound respect due to His Majesty, alternating with vague and soothing medical prescriptions guaranteed in any event to be perfectly harmless.

Meanwhile the disease was taking its course, and Toung-Tche, preserved by tradition from the too attentive ministrations of his physicians, might possibly, thanks to his youth and constitution, have contrived a natural recovery, had he not one night, when barely entering into convalescence, conceived the crazy idea of escaping from his imperial couch and a boredom in which he was at any rate warm and sheltered, in order to creep forth in bitterly cold weather and seek adventure in the slums of the Chinese Quarter.

The results of this escapade were not long delayed. At dawn the Son of Heaven was borne back to his palace gasping, with glassy eyes, and a violent fever. He was hastily laid upon his state bed and messengers despatched to inform the Dowager Empress that her Son was about to ascend the Dragon's Chariot.

At this news Tseu-Hi displayed admirable composure and self-possession.

Without a moment's delay, she despatched a secret messenger to Li-Houng-Tchang, the viceroy of Pet-chili, ordering him to mobilise his troops and to march immediately to Peking; she then informed Yong-Lou of the course of events and begged him to station his Manchu Guards along the principal thoroughfares of the Tartar Town and at all the gates of the Forbidden City; finally, in the Violet Town itself, she rallied all the eunuchs to arms. Having thus attended to every possible detail, she calmly awaited events.

The Holy Man lingered throughout the day, thus affording his venerable mother plenty of time in which to execute point by point her various military preparations; it was not until afternoon that he made up his mind to turn his august countenance towards the South, in order that his last breath should at any rate be taken in a seemly manner and in accordance with tradition.

The Woman Who Commanded

Informed of the event, the Empress Tseu-Hi, assuming the white garments of deep mourning, came solemnly to offer funeral honours to her divine Son, and after the prostrations and lamentations prescribed by ritual, she insisted on placing on his feet with her own hands the new slippers required for his long journey.

Beside her, the Empress Consort, determined to appear genuinely bereaved, uttered shrill shrieks which had no softening effect upon her masterful mother-in-law; while behind the two women stood all the members of the imperial family, also displaying extreme distress, while inwardly debating the wisest political course to steer in their individual personal interests.

The Empress Tseu-Ngan, who had upon this occasion been granted permission to leave the Palace of the East, where she had remained a prisoner ever since the assassination of the Grand Eunuch Ngan-Te-Hai, was perhaps the only living soul to feel any genuine and deep distress at the passing of this Holy Man whose childhood had been her especial care.

It was an amazing fact, but she alone had retained a true and disinterested affection for Toung-Tche, despite the fact that he was the son of her detested rival. She had begun by watching over him solely in the interests of the Dynasty, but little by little, in the process of guiding his early steps, she had become profoundly attached to him.

Five Hundred Million Men

Thus Toung-Tche, leaving this wicked earth, was mourned only by his own mother's most deadly enemy!

For the remainder of his family his death was an immense relief and opened up an agreeable prospect of freedom to indulge long-curbed ambitions.

CHAPTER TWELVE

Immediately after the fulfilment of the initial ceremonies in honour of the illustrious departed, the entire imperial family repaired to the Palace of Intellectual Nourishment, there to deliberate, in the presence of the high state officials, the question of the political situation.

In accordance with age-old custom, the Dragon's Throne could not remain vacant, even for a day, and it was necessary that the decree announcing to the people the death of the Holy Man, should also proclaim his successor.

In the foremost rank of the assembly Prince Tsaï-Tche, a descendant of the eldest son of the Emperor Tao-Kouang, preened himself while advancing the rights of his son Pou-Louen. Beside him sat Prince Kuong, son of that same Tao-Kouang and brother to the Emperor Hien-Foung, who, as Regent, preferred the claims of his own son.

More modestly in the background lurked Prince Tchouen, younger brother of Prince Kuong, whose only trump in the game was his marriage to the sister of Tseu-Hi.

Finally, the Empress Consort, Ha-Lou-To, was inalterably determined that no one should usurp the

rights of the imperial child which she was so soon
to bear.

Near her, ready to support her, sat Tseu-Ngan,
Empress of the East, hoping to witness the final
decline of the star of the Empress of the West.

Meanwhile, Tseu-Hi, taking the bull by the horns,
began proceedings by assuming the presidency of the
august assembly; imposing silence, she invited
Prince Tsaï-Tche to speak. Prince Kuong followed
with a justification of his own claim, but Prince
Tchouen merely threw himself at the feet of the Empress Tseu-Hi, begging her to act as she thought
best. At which juncture, Ha-Lou-To, convulsed with
fury, quitted her place and standing proudly before
Tseu-Hi, cried:

"The only legal heir must be the son of Toung-
Tche! In a few days' time, I shall become Empress
Dowager and in accordance with custom, assume the
Regency."

Without moving a muscle, Tseu-Hi replied coldly:

"In the first place, where is the proof that you
will bear a son? . . . And in any event, even should
you do so, we could not await his birth, since any
interregnum is forbidden by dynastic law."

At these words Ha-Lou-To's numerous partisans
murmured in a manner that was hardly respectful to
Tseu-Hi.

Thus encouraged, the adherents of Prince Tsaï-
Tche and those of Prince Kuong also began to pro-

test, saying that Tseu-Hi had no right to decide, of her own initiative, the fate of the Empire.

Whereupon Ha-Lou-To returned to the attack.

"So long as the Empress Dowager remains among us, there will be nothing but discord. . . ."

And she added perfidiously:

"And little she cares, so long as she can reign!"

Tseu-Hi replied impassively:

"Since the majority of my son Toung-Tche, I had voluntarily renounced all authority. . . . I was diffident and wished to be certain once and for all whether or not I was indispensable to the prosperity of the Celestial Empire. . . . Now I call you all to witness, Princes of the Blood, and you, high state officials, what has occurred since my retirement? . . . Have the courage to admit that everything has been going from bad to worse, that public affairs are badly conducted, that rebellion is beginning to raise its head and that wherever you care to look, evil passions and new intrigues are arising, while you yourselves are here and now giving an example of disorder and confusion."

At this severe admonition, the members of the assembly quivered and looks that were charged with hatred were directed at this foolhardy woman who did not hesitate publicly to upbraid all their personal foibles.

There was a general chorus of asseverations that regardless of the systematic obstructions raised by

Tseu-Hi, it was time for the assembly to make a decision.

Believing that victory was in sight, Ha-Lou-To announced:

"If it becomes necessary, might shall assist right."

"I entirely agree with you, Madam," replied Tseu-Hi, with a bow and smile that gained in irony from the fact that at that very moment Marshal Yong-Lou, whom no one had seen fit to invite to this intimate gathering, had joined the assembly as an uninvited guest.

Drawing himself proudly to the full height of his tall figure, and folding his arms:

"I await orders," said he, in ringing tones.

But no one risked any reply, since his remark was accompanied from without by the sound of warlike cries and the clashing of swords.

He resumed:

"The army of the viceroy of Petchili which has just entered the Tartar Town is also awaiting orders."

And every man and woman present realised that the only hope of safety lay in not further offending Tseu-Hi who had so securely prepared her coup d'état.

Solemnly she reopened the discussion with the announcement:

"The new Holy Man will be my own nephew, the son of my sister and of Prince Tchouen. . . . He will reign under the name of Kouang-Siu . . . I have said!"

And imperiously brandishing the Seal of Transmitted Legitimate Authority, she commanded:

"Let the necessary decree be immediately prepared, in order that I may affix the Seal."

Not a member of the assembly ventured to utter a word, while Prince Tchouen more dead than alive with pride and joy threw himself at Tseu-Hi's feet to thank her for her signal favour.

But Marshal Yong-Lou, who had learned satire from long association with Tseu-Hi, suggested in bantering tones:

"Why not put it to the vote? Would it not be a more regular proceeding?"

Tseu-Hi smilingly agreed to this pleasant fancy.

Then Prince Kuong, who tenaciously held to his rights and knew not the meaning of fear, rose in his seat and in a firm voice voted against Tseu-Hi's candidate. . . .

He was, moreover, alone in doing so.

The Empress, who passionately adored courage and who, on the other hand, could well afford to be merciful, turned towards her only opponent, saying gently:

"You have as usual, Prince Kuong, given evidence that you are a stranger to fear . . . and I feel no resentment towards you. . . . You will, as in the past, assist me in the Regency . . . but for the moment your duty is to relieve the guard in the mortuary chamber of the Holy Man!"

Thus furnished with an honorable pretext for withdrawal, Prince Kuong quitted the assembly with dignity, and went to take up his official post as guardian of the mortal remains of Toung-Tche.

In his heart he was bound to admit that so far as concerned the good of the Empire, a Sovereign such as Tseu-Hi was preferable to any new puppet! Now that the die was definitely cast he intended to serve this amazing super-woman as loyally as he had done aforetime.

Meanwhile messengers had been hastily despatched to fetch the new Son of Heaven, the divine Kouang-Siu, from his father's house, and the small child was brought with great ceremony to be presented to the Empress Dowager.

As the hour was a late one, he was already half asleep, blinking his eyes and completely bewildered. . . . He was none the less compelled to perform all the traditional genuflexions before his venerable aunt and to stammer the suitable little oration that was whispered in his ear by his worthy father, Prince Tchouen.

The new Holy Man was then conducted to the mortuary chamber of his predecessor, there to render the customary funeral honours.

Unfortunately, at this solemn moment, the little boy began to evince a most unseemly indiscipline. . . .

The Woman Who Commanded

Seized with terror at the sight of the corpse in the wavering greenish half-light cast by the mortuary candles, he burst into floods of tears and, oblivious of ritual, begged to be taken away at once.

He was only quieted when his venerable aunt Tseu-Hi whispered in his ear that, Holy Man as he was, she would whip him till he bled if he continued to display such unseemly lack of control and did not obey her implicitly.

This threat, frequently followed by its execution, was often to be repeated in the future, for Tseu-Hi had no intention of allowing even a shadow of resistance to her authority to arise in this new Son of Heaven whom she herself had set upon the Dragon's Throne!

CHAPTER THIRTEEN

After her celebrated coup d'état, Tseu-Hi had good hopes of quietly exercising an authority that none would dare to contest.

Prince Tsaï-Tche, realising the futility of opposition, had sensibly withdrawn the candidature of his son Pou-Louen and only desired to live on good terms with the Empress Dowager who, by her masterly energy, had captured his respect and his admiration.

As for Prince Kuong, he had also and without any afterthoughts definitely allied himself to the astounding dictator.

The only remaining anxiety lay in the fact that the Empress Ha-Lou-To might yet complicate matters by bearing a son whom it would be difficult to relegate to a subsidiary position; but Tseu-Hi had already made up her mind to overcome this trifling obstacle, and was quite prepared to commit a crime if necessary rather than allow her daughter-in-law to dispute her authority.

It was therefore with a serene mind that she prepared herself on the morning following the assembly of the Grand Council, to receive an emissary who ceremoniously delivered into her hands a weighty document emanating from the Court of Censors and countersigned by the Tribunal of Rites. The doyen of the Imperial Censors, the most virtuous Ou-Ko-Tou, had courageously considered it incumbent upon him to address a long memorandum to the Empress Tseu-Hi, in which he respectfully explained his reason for regarding the election of Kouang-Siu as contrary to the law and customs of the Empire.

According to his view, it was Prince Pou-Louen, as representing the senior branch of the Dynasty, who should have ascended the Dragon's Throne; he alone, moreover, being of a later generation than the Emperor Toung-Tche, was qualified to offer that sovereign the ritual ancestral worship; Kouang-Siu, as a mere first cousin, could not be regarded as a posthumous heir. The unfortunate Toung-Tche would therefore remain without legally adoptive progeny, a situation which was, in the view of the Censor, of unprecedented gravity.

In conclusion, would it not have been preferable, ignoring the question of interregnum, to await the confinement of the Empress Ha-Lou-To who might well give birth to a legitimate heir to the Emperor Toung-Tche?

There followed a thousand further explications and political considerations, both religious and moral, one more boring and involved than another.

Reading this indigestible document, Tseu-Hi merely shrugged her shoulders, perfectly determined to ignore these tactless observations. For her part, the matter being now safely accomplished, the old dotard was at liberty to employ his leisure in the futile pastime of inditing criticisms that could have no practical consequences.

According to her usual custom, she wrote to the Imperial Censor informing him that she had taken note of his judicial observations, but that since the composition of this remarkable opus must have exhausted his failing strength, she begged him to oblige her by seeking a country retreat where he might be suitably cared for.

She was congratulating herself upon having thus closed the incident, when the insufferable ancient had the bad taste to commit suicide in an ostentatious manner, with a view to emphasising his memorandum to which he obstinately adhered.

Much annoyed by this melodrama, which was an inauspicious prelude to her recovered Regency, Tseu-Hi thought it wise to accord a partial submission to one portion at any rate of the suicide's contentions. She published a decree to the effect that Kouang-Siu's first son should become the posthumous heir of Toung-Tche. Since Kouang-Siu was only four years of age, it was in point of fact postponing the solution of the problem to a fairly distant date, but the decree fulfilled its official purpose, and enabled Tseu-Hi to pose as having bowed before the decision of the Tribunal of Rites and the Court of Censors, which afforded a fine example of respect for tradition.

On the other hand, in order to avoid other and perhaps more serious annoyances, she decided to lose no time in despatching her daughter-in-law, Ha-Lou-To upon the long journey. The sex of the expected imperial offspring would thus become a matter of small importance! Obviously the problem would find its own solution in the event of Ha-Lou-To giving birth to a daughter, but Tseu-Hi intended to run no risks of its proving to be a boy.

She therefore gave secret orders to the Grand Eunuch Li-Lien-Yn, for the immediate suppression of the Empress Ha-Lou-To.

Accordingly, a few days later, that unfortunate Sovereign was attacked by a mysterious illness to which she succumbed in a matter of hours.

Ha-Lou-To had had small doubts as to her eventual fate from the moment when she had so obstinately defied her mother-in-law, but she had not believed that Tseu-Hi would be so shameless as to destroy in the womb the imperial infant in whose veins ran her own blood, and who would have been her only grandson.

Never having felt the slightest affection for her son, Tseu-Hi had no hankerings to be a grandmother and no intention of indulging domestic sentimentality at the price of that authority which she undoubtedly considered indispensable to the honour of her Dynasty and to her country's salvation.

She had, above everything, the soul of an Empress,

ready to meet every emergency, as she was resolved to commit every crime, rather than sacrifice, even for an instant, that supreme authority which she honestly believed to have been bestowed upon her from Above.

CHAPTER FOURTEEN

A few peaceful years elapsed before any new annoyance arose to disturb Tseu-Hi in the exercise of a power which she wielded to the general satisfaction of all those subjects who continued to venerate her as their providential "old buddha."

She daily presided with incomparable dignity at the morning sittings of the Grand Council, surprising the most experienced statesmen by the far-seeing wisdom of her judgment; she also took a personal share in the drafting of the more important imperial decrees, after minute study of all memoranda addressed to the Throne by the governors of the various provinces. Always skilful at finding the best and most prompt solution to the thorniest of problems, she unravelled the most complicated political tangles with bewildering facility.

She was in fact an extraordinary woman, and her worst enemies, while enumerating her excesses and her crimes, have never been able to deny her genius.

The arduous daily labour which she assumed as head of the government in no way prevented Tseu-Hi from remaining, in her hours of relaxation, the most exquisite of women.

She possessed so natural and potent an attraction

that she was able immediately to charm all those who approached her, so that it was almost with pleasure that any notable personage meekly submitted to decapitation by the State Executioner sooner than annoy so lovely a woman by vain recriminations. For if she loved to conquer hearts, she was equally disposed on occasion to cut off heads without the slightest compunction; but no one bore her any resentment, such was the amiability and elegance with which she gave the order for execution.

Everyone was quick to realize that she acted neither from cruelty nor revengefulness, but from an obvious necessity to reinforce her authority from time to time by a certain demonstration of energy.

Moreover, she was so deeply loved and honoured that even an impulse of ill-humour would have been comprehended and forgiven.

When work was over, she gave herself equally enthusiastically to pleasures, for she was determined to live every moment of her existence.

She had a fine taste for poetry, for painting and for the theatre, but she was equally appreciative of the less ethereal pleasures of bed and board. With knowledge of every vice, she did no more than brush the fringes of excess, invariably returning to a healthy viewpoint. If, for instance, it pleased her to sample delicately the rarest and most highly spiced dishes, she had the good sense never to allow such extravagances to alienate her from the ordinary domestic fare whose homely and substantial qualities comfort the appetite without harming the digestion.

In matters of love the same thing obtained; although she never feared to seek in the company of her women and her castrates the most eccentric sensations, while giving free play to her vivid imagination, she always returned with delight to the virile and faithful affection of Marshal Yong-Lou who, being of an uncomplicated temperament, had been content simply and fervently to worship her since her earliest childhood.

She had, as a matter of fact, consented to his contracting a conventional marriage in order to ensure the continuation of his line and the birth of sons to accord him ancestral honours, but she would never have been reconciled to the thought of his taking a mistress or even an ordinary concubine.

And how, indeed, could such an idea have entered the mind of a privileged lover who had the prodigious good fortune to retain the affections of the loveliest woman in China?

Tseu-Hi, sure of herself and convinced of her superiority over any conceivable rival, could not even entertain the supposition that Yong-Lou might ever prove unfaithful.

For what possible reason should such a man, profoundly loyal and entirely devoted to his mistress, betray her to whom he owed not only the most exquisite hours of his existence but also his phenomenal career? Was he not the chosen among all others, the friend of childhood, the intimate confidant of every joy and of every sorrow!

Together they had grown up, loved, hoped and suffered! A thousand precious memories recalled to them a painful or delightful past, their hearts beat in unison; their ideas, their beliefs, their very prejudices were identical; never had the slightest dissension arisen to sever them; they deeply admired and respected one another, and if Tseu-Hi had been instrumental in the rise of Yong-Lou, he, on his side, had saved her life on several occasions and had always succoured her in the gravest emergencies; they therefore owed each other a mutual gratitude and never failed most tenderly to express it.

Physically, they were also made for one another: they had the same beauty, the same vitality and were of the same age. Their love was strong and true and raised them both above degrading and commonplace emotions; it kept their bodies healthy and their minds clean and united their spirits in a fine enthusiasm.

However, while the all-powerful Tseu-Hi, fortunate in love as in politics, lived an intensely vital existence in a positive blaze of adulation, the wretched Tseu-Ngan, permanently deprived of all authority, had once more been allotted the unsatisfactory task of supervising the education of the Holy Man.

The Woman Who Commanded

Having an ingrained passion for the grandeur of the dynasty, she brought to her mission the same intense enthusiasm that had animated her when watching over the childhood of Toung-Tche.

Since it appeared to be her fate to prepare the future Sons of Heaven for a worthy exercise of the Supreme Power, she endeavoured in a noble spirit of duty to rise to the height of her sacred mission. All of which did not prevent her from nursing in her embittered heart a silent hatred of the Empress of the West whose principal aim seemed always to be the destruction of the stars in her firmament.

She ardently desired to satisfy this hatred which she had nourished for so many years. Too weak to attempt an open attack upon the Empress of the West, she resolved upon a master-stroke of treachery which would wound her enemy to the heart and afford her ample revenge for all the humiliations that she had endured.

Among her maids of honour there was at that time a young virgin of marvellous beauty and irresistible charm. Tseu-Ngan perfidiously contrived that this amiable person, whom she had carefully primed and bribed with promises of promotion, should be in evidence on every occasion when Yong-Lou, in the course of his duties, came to the Palace of the East.

Of an ardent temperament, the marshal could hardly remain insensible to the engaging smiles of this peerless beauty. Despite the deep and enduring love that he bore to Tseu-Hi, he could not refrain from the reflection that this exquisite young girl, who appeared so generously inclined, was a very tempting prey.

One day, as though by chance, the two found themselves alone together, Tseu-Ngan having retired under pretext of a slight indisposition: well trained by her mistress, the maid of honour sank almost swooning into Yong-Lou's arms, and he, for the first time in his life, lacked the necessary brutality to repulse her.

Uttering tender murmurs, she clasped her arms round the neck of the unfortunate warrior who was quite unable to withstand such an assault. Within a few moments he had capitulated, and although deeply ashamed of his own weakness, he was compelled to admit that he had found great enjoyment in the episode.

It was, in point of fact, repeated on several occasions during the following moon.

Yong-Lou, however, suffered deep remorse for his infidelity to Tseu-Hi, and was moreover not without anxiety as to the consequences should she ever come to know of his escapade.

His youthful mistress might do her utmost to persuade him that she had taken every needful precaution to keep their liaison a profound secret, he knew by long experience that such matters always end by being discovered, in an enclosure where every corner conceals a spy and where the walls themselves have ears.

Exposure was all the more inevitable in that Tseu-Ngan, who had pulled the wires of the intrigue, was only biding her time. And yet, curiously enough, the scandal broke out unexpectedly and in the most foolish manner, by the act of the austere Weng-Toung-Ho, official tutor to the young Kouang-Siu.

This worthy scholar, his spectacles goggling above his flat nose, was desperately pursuing the Holy Man who had surreptitiously concealed himself in order to avoid the study of a classical commentary which he considered peculiarly tedious; tactlessly and without warning, believing that he had discovered the lair of the recalcitrant pupil, the old man upset a screen that masked the lovers' tender intercourse.

Scandalised at his discovery, the imperial tutor raised his arms to heaven, while the terrified younger delinquent made matters worse by uttering a piercing shriek which brought a flock of eunuchs and servants to his assistance. Tseu-Ngan herself also made her appearance with every evidence of indignation, but Yong-Lou was not deceived. He understood at last the nature of the snare with which he had so foolishly allowed himself to be trapped.

Resigning himself to his fate, he made no appeal for a secrecy that would in any case have been out of the question; he went straight to the Palace of

Perpetual Spring in order to tell Tseu-Hi the truth
and await his well-deserved punishment.

Nevertheless, from seemliness and also in deep
compassion for the pain which he was about to inflict,
he resolved to use infinite tact in the admission of
his fault; but his resolve was vain, for at the very
first word he uttered, Tseu-Hi realised the entire
situation.

She grew very pale; her features were terribly
convulsed, and her breath came in gasps as though
she were about to die. Speechless, Yong-Lou knelt
before her with bent head, like a criminal before his
judge. He knew the Empress too well to be under
any delusions regarding her feelings; he knew that
never had she forgotten or forgiven an injury, and
that his doom was already sealed, but it was not for
himself that he suffered! He would gladly have
given his life on the spot if the sacrifice could have
lessened the pain of her whom he once more loved
with unabated passion. How could he ever have
been so cowardly as to betray the trust that she had
always so generously accorded him! . . . No torture could ever be sufficiently cruel for the expiation
of such a crime!

Meanwhile Tseu-Hi had regained her self-possession; in a toneless voice she said with perfect simplicity:

"In whom shall I henceforth place any trust, now

that you, the friend of my childhood, have unworthily betrayed me!"

And fearing lest she should weep, she proudly withdrew and left him.

CHAPTER FIFTEEN

In spite of the terrible wound inflicted both upon her pride and her affections, a wound from which she was never entirely to recover, Tseu-Hi could not bring herself to order the death of him who had so cruelly betrayed her, but whom she still loved with a deep devotion.

She merely removed her favour, depriving him by public decree of all his titles and emoluments and at the same time forbidding him to commit suicide, as he would normally have been expected to do after a scandal of such dimensions.

In this manner she proved to him that if the offended Empress was compelled to punish, the woman, on the other hand, however deeply wounded, had the generosity to refrain from vengeance, and even to cherish the offender in the innermost sanctuary of her heart.

Moved to tears by such nobility, Yong-Lou went sadly forth into exile, debarred by iron-bound tradition from any parting interview at which he might for the last time have expressed his bitter repentance to her whom he had so dearly loved.

Tseu-Hi was thus deprived of her best friend and her most assiduous protector. It was with infinite regret that she beheld the departure from Peking of the man who recalled to her her ardent youth and who had so often generously afforded her help and assistance.

If, however, she had seen fit to be merciful with regard to Yong-Lou, such was not the case when it became a question of the Empress of the East who had so traitorously destroyed her happiness. The latter, assuming an air of complete innocence, in vain tried to disclaim all responsibility in the adventure; she was quite unsuccessful in deceiving her rival who was much too shrewd not to have immediately grasped the true facts.

Unwilling to lower herself by a display of jealousy toward a creature of no importance, Tseu-Hi disdained to execute the pretty doll whom the Empress of the East had employed to trap Yong-Lou; but she concentrated all her rage against Tseu-Ngan, who alone, in her eyes, had been responsible for the entire catastrophe.

Seeking her rival in the Palace of the East, she attacked her even more furiously than she had done on the occasion of the murder of her favourite, the Grand Eunuch Ngan-Te-Hai.

Reminding her of that earlier crime, she announced haughtily:

"I was weak enough at that time to extend to you a measure of mercy and to content myself with hurling in your face my utter contempt. I ought to have thought of the future, and I should rightly have punished you then as you deserved. When a snake has struck once, it is not sufficient to confine it, one should crush it out of existence. I lacked that forethought; it was an error for which I have had to pay dearly; but I shall not be so foolish as to repeat it. . . . Your days, Madam, are numbered, you have not long in which to behold the sun. . . . Accept the warning and lose no time in making such preparations as you may think seemly for the long journey you will shortly take."

Having thus clearly pronounced sentence of death upon her terrified rival, Tseu-Hi returned to her Palace of Perpetual Spring and sent at once for the Grand Eunuch Li-Lien-Yn, in order to convey to him her orders for the prompt suppression of the Empress Tseu-Ngan.

"You will," she commanded, "act with discretion, as in the case of the Empress Ha-Lou-To. The choice of a poison and of a suitable hour I leave entirely in your hands."

Li-Lien-Yn, who detested the Empress of the East and who, moreover, had not forgotten the fate meted out by her to his unhappy predecessor, was certainly not the person to protest against an order which he regarded as essential to his personal safety.

A few days later, it became known in the Forbidden City, that the Empress Tseu-Ngan had contracted the mysterious illness of which the Empress Ha-Lou-

The Woman Who Commanded

To had recently died: the news surprised no one! Ever since the disgrace of Yong-Lou, of which many suspicioned the true cause, bad news had been expected regarding the health of the Empress of the East.

The latter remained conscious until her last breath.

She was in no doubt as to the nature of her illness and immediately realised that the Empress of the West had carried out her threat of the preceding week.

For reasons of state and out of respect for the dignity of the Imperial House, she refrained from recording the fact in the official Testament which she indited. She desired in this manner to convey to her shameless rival a final lesson in deportment, and to prove herself worthy by her nobility of soul, of her high station.

She therefore contented herself with recalling the fact that she had always voluntarily subordinated herself to the interests of the Dragon's Throne, and she begged that her interment should be modest in conformity with her life.

A few moments later she laid herself upon the traditional state bed, and turning her face toward the South in accordance with the prescribed ritual, she calmly awaited the end.

Tseu-Hi was extremely punctilious, after the expiration of the court mourning, in causing to be ceremoniously transported to the Eastern Imperial

Tombs the magnificent coffin with which she had provided her rival; for this secretly murdered woman must ever remain, in the eyes of the people, the venerable widow of the glorious Emperor Hien-Foung.

The Woman Who Commanded

CHAPTER SIXTEEN

In the absence of the regrettably exiled Yong-Lou, Tseu-Hi could depend upon the personal protection and absolute loyalty of Li-Houng-Tchang, whom she had been shrewd enough to appoint as Governor of Petchili in recompense for his services against the Taï-Ping.

Taught by experience and having formerly observed among the paleface Barbarians the incontestable superiority of their armaments, Li-Houng-Tchang had persuaded the Empress Tseu-Hi to look with favour upon a complete reform of the army which he was to command. Very soon, having instructed and equipped his troops in the modern manner, he was confidently able to assure Tseu-Hi of his power to resist any and every insurrection that might arise in the vast Celestial Empire, and was, moreover, confident of crushing any rebellion that might break out in the province of Peking.

Her mind at rest upon this all-important point, Tseu-Hi was at liberty fearlessly to exercise any measure of authority. This she did not fail to do, for with every added experience she acquired a greater conviction that an iron hand was needed to preserve peace and order in the Celestial Empire.

Five Hundred Million Men

The slightest weakness, the smallest hesitation, might lead to the overthrow of the Throne and a reign of appalling anarchy. Of that she was firmly convinced, and that her conviction was not unjustified has since been evidenced by the actual conditions in China.

But where she fell into the same error as Li-Houng-Tchang was in believing that because her troops possessed modern armaments she was in a position to fight successfully against foreign soldiers.

She was very soon to receive the first shattering proof of this error.

An enthusiastic nationalist, she supported the policy of "Greater China" and was persuaded to attempt a defence of the sovereign rights which China had possessed from time immemorial over neighbouring countries. This policy promptly brought her up against Japan over the question of Korea.

More prudent than the Empress, Li-Houng-Tchang temporarily avoided war with the "Japanese dwarfs" (as the Chinese contemptuously called them) by paying them a large indemnity and by agreeing to share with them the control of Korea, but he was unable to evade war with the French who were completing the conquest of Indo-China by establishing themselves at Tonkin in defiance of every Chinese claim on that country.

In the absence of railways, Li-Houng-Tchang was unable to send his army to the distant southern frontiers, and in any case, to do so would have left Peking dangerously exposed; he began to realise that it is not sufficient to have well-equipped troops, it is also needful to move them.

As for what befell the Chinese fleet, it was nothing short of immediate disaster. Admiral Courbet, rapidly sweeping the China Seas, seized Formosa and the Pescadores and landed almost unopposed at Fouchou.

Realising the futility of the struggle, Li-Houng-Tchang persuaded Tseu-Hi to sign a peace with France and to bow before the inevitable, that is to say, the permanent establishment of an Occidental power in Indo-China.

But from that hour he nursed the thought of the necessity for railways, both for the defence of a vast empire and for its commercial development. And he was later to impose his views in this matter upon the Empress, who, for all her conservative spirit, was far too intelligent not to realise the absolute need for modern progress in China, if she were to hold her own as a greater power.

Convinced that Li-Houng-Tchang, for all his failure against France, was the only associate she required in her exercise of Supreme Authority, Tseu-Hi got rid of Prince Kuong and his colleagues on the Grand Council by the trenchant means of a single and comprehensive decree in which she denounced their notorious incapacity to face a situation which the march of modern civilisation was daily rendering more complicated. She then elected a Grand Council of entirely new members, all of them devotedly loyal to her person if somewhat jealous among themselves; a fact which increased her domination by enabling her at need to set one against another. From that time onwards, under the nominal aegis of her brother-in-law, Prince Tchouen, who had, contrary to all precedent, supplanted his elder, Prince Kuong, as Grand Councillor to the Throne, she governed in a manner so entirely personal and autocratic that History may vainly be searched for a parallel.

And when one reflects that she thus controlled five hundred million subjects who, under every reign but hers, had invariably seethed with a terrible spirit of anarchy and rebellion, as indeed they are doing at the present time, one remains spellbound before the brilliant genius of this super-woman.

CHAPTER SEVENTEEN

There came, however, a time when Kouang-Siu, having attained the age of eighteeen years, could no longer with decency be kept in leading-strings by his venerable aunt, the Empress Tseu-Hi.

Much against her will, she was forced to announce his majority and to invest him with the shadow if not the substance of authority (1887).

For another two years, however, she continued to govern exactly as though the Holy Man had not existed; then she suddenly made up her mind to retire, having previously united the Holy Man to her favourite niece, Long-You, daughter of her younger brother who had become the imposing but innocuous Duke Kouei-Siang.

Remembering the error which she had formerly committed in marrying her son Toung-Tche to the ungrateful Ha-Lou-To who had so deceived her with her assumed airs of modesty and submission, Tseu-Hi had on this occasion carefully ascertained that the new Empress Consort would not equally play her false.

Before promoting her, Tseu-Hi had most meticulously tested the personal loyalty of her niece, and had, moreover, exacted from her a solemn oath upon the spirits of their common ancestors, that she would always remain obedient to her aunt's commands, serving her interests, even against those of Kouang-Siu, should occasion arise.

The fact was that Tseu-Hi, with the assistance of her niece, fully intended to retain dominion over the Holy Man, to have foreknowledge of his every action, and to be informed of his most secret intentions.

Having thus carefully arranged the political situation, Tseu-Hi left the Palace of Perpetual Spring and retired to the Summer Palace, which she was busily engaged in restoring to all its pristine glory.

It was in this lovely retreat that she had known the greatest happiness of her life. In the autumn of her days, she hoped to re-evoke some of the emotions of springtime. She was, indeed, now fifty-five years of age, but in this amazing woman nature seemed to have made a happy exception, and Tseu-Hi enjoyed the astonishing blessing of having remained as youthful in body as in mind; age had touched neither her appearance nor her emotions; she looked barely forty and was still in the prime of her brilliant beauty.

Nevertheless, she realised that the sun of the passions that still burnt within her was declining toward the horizon and that no power on earth could arrest its course. But she was fully determined that it should set in a blaze of glory!

Relieved of material cares and of political responsibilities, she desired only to be a great lover while there was still time for love.

Unfortunately Yong-Lou had left Peking in obedience to that imperial decree which she now so deeply deplored. Undeniably, her lover's conduct had demanded exemplary punishment, but had not Tseu-Hi most severely punished herself by the exile of a lover whom she was utterly unable to forget?

Already, moderating her earlier decision, Tseu-Hi had restored to Yong-Lou his honours and titles and had appointed him Grand Tartar Marshal in the province of Chen-Si; but so far a lingering feeling of wounded self-esteem had restrained her from recalling him to her side.

But how intensely she missed his presence! Thinking of him, in that Summer Palace which had witnessed their passionate embraces, her blood seemed like fire in her veins.

Great waves of desire overwhelmed her; a strange fever seemed to intensify the acuteness of all her senses.

And she was alone, alone in this magnificent imperial residence where her youthful love should have consumed her in its clear white flame!

There came an evening when, leaning upon the white marble balustrade above the waters that glowed with the dying fires of day, she reflected upon the fires that devoured her inwardly, but of which she so deeply dreaded the extinction. Making a sudden decision, she summoned the Grand Eunuch Li-Lien-Yn, and began to whisper mysteriously in his ear. Whereupon, having received her commands, he stole away into the shadows on silent feet to fulfil the delicate mission with which he had been entrusted.

If the truth must be told, Li-Lien-Yn would gladly have dispensed with this particular mark of confidence. He made his way in some anxiety toward the high walls of the Tartar Town, recalling without enthusiasm the parting instructions of Tseu-Hi:

"And above all things you must be both skilful and discreet. . . . Your position, your very life may be at stake! . . ."

It is not always plain sailing to be the intimate confidant of an Empress!

The Woman Who Commanded

CHAPTER EIGHTEEN

Tseu-Hi had resumed her reflective attitude, leaning upon the white marble balustrade of the balcony above the lake before the Summer Palace.

Night was now approaching; a yellow moon, rising from a misty horizon, was reflected in the lake like an enormous orange and the first stars appeared in the darkening heavens.

The light was gentle and mysterious, like that of a shaded temple lamp; a distant sound of love songs came from a countryside that lay entranced in the quietude of a wonderful summer night, and close to where Tseu-Hi was standing, drops of dew fell like shooting stars from the feathery foliage of the willows.

The Empress studied the heavens with an insistent gaze, for the Grand Astronomer attached to her household had recently sent her a report to the effect that upon this and succeeding nights, the Star of the Imperial House would be in conjunction with the Planet of Love, which might certainly be regarded as a favourable conjunction.

Absorbed in contemplation, Tseu-Hi thus passed the early nocturnal hours. But as the Hour of the Tiger drew near, she became anxious: had the Grand

Astronomer possibly been mistaken? Li-Lien-Yn appeared to be taking an unconscionable time over his errand! Could he possibly have failed in his mission?

Suddenly she started: he stood at her side, having issued like a ghost from the darkness.

She questioned him in an undertone:

"Have you succeeded?"

Observing that he nodded his head, she added:

"Who is it? . . . And where is he?"

"He is a perfectly enchanting young man," whispered Li-Lien Yn; "I conducted him to the pavilion on the Central Island where I left him, begging him to await my return."

"Does he know that he is to see me?"

"Certainly not. . . . He has not the slightest idea. I merely told him that one of your ladies-in-waiting wished to make his acquaintance, having deeply admired the poem which he had composed for the last triennial competition. . . . The poor fool was so flattered in his literary vanity that he was quite willing to follow me. . . . I told him, moreover, that his admirer was a young woman of astounding beauty so that he will not be surprised at seeing Your Majesty!"

And the Grand Eunuch closed this skilful compliment by a delighted chuckle.

But Tseu-Hi was not without anxiety regarding the outcome of this adventure. She was expected to play the part of an amorous maiden, which was flattering but might prove difficult.

Moreover, she would be able to judge whether, appearing to the young man as a mere maid of honour, her unaided charms were really adequate to the occasion. Here was a genuine opportunity of discovering whether the passionate admiration meted out to her by all her courtiers was genuine or assumed!

Rather perturbed at this reflection, Tseu-Hi nevertheless made up her mind to follow the Grand Eunuch who led her across the marble bridge to the Central Island.

On the threshold of the pavilion she paused a moment and appeared to hesitate; then, having applied a touch of colour to the spot of vivid scarlet placed, as was customary, under her lower lip, she swiftly entered the building. Li-Lien-Yn had not deceived her; the young man who awaited her was really attractive. He was placidly seated in a corner of the apartment, serenely nibbling at the watermelon seeds that the Grand Eunuch had placed in a saucer before him to help him while away the time of waiting.

Tseu-Hi remarked with tenderness the delicacy of his features, his unclouded brow, his elegantly arched and pencilled eyebrows. His eyes were almond-shaped and his mouth was like a crimson cherry beneath his amusingly flat little nose.

From the crown of his carefully shaven head

depended his long pigtail, which lost itself like a serpent among the folds of his silken tunic, proving that he was as cleanly as he was elegant.

Other pleasing details of his appearance struck Tseu-Hi, who remarked with pleasure that he possessed the aristocratic hands of a scholar.

As soon as he perceived Tseu-Hi, he began to simper:

"This must surely be some heavenly apparition . . . such beauty is far too rare for our humble earth."

She bowed graciously.

"Delightful poet, you behold in me your humble servant. . . ."

And in several elegantly turned phrases she complimented him warmly upon his remarkable literary talent.

The young man was not unduly surprised, since his modest air did not arise from any doubt of his genius: in his innocence he even considered it quite natural that a lovely woman should desire to give him proof of her admiration.

Without a shadow of mistrust he therefore initiated a gallant assault upon a fortress that had little intention of resistance. At which juncture the Grand Eunuch, who had remained within call, discreetly withdrew on tiptoe to the marble bridge where he could listen to the love songs of the frogs among the lotus leaves.

And the last hour of the night flew by, and still Tseu-Hi remained in the pavilion of love.

Dawn was breaking and its roses were falling from heaven upon the curved gables of the Summer Palace.

Li-Lien-Yn anxiously reflected that his divine mistress ran a risk of compromising her edifying reputation as an "old buddha," when he suddenly beheld her appear, fresh and lively as a bird that greets the limpid air of morning.

With a gesture of satisfaction she gave him to understand from afar that all had been for the best in this best of all possible worlds and hastened away in the direction of the Summer Palace.

It was left for the Grand Eunuch to entertain the young man, who, all unknowing, had enjoyed the tremendous honour of an Empress' favour.

With exquisite courtesy, he was offered a cup of that tea which his host was so skilful at preparing and which was guaranteed to insure a lover's discretion.

As soon as the poet, after some moments of painful convulsions, had drawn his final breath, Li-Lien-Yn carefully attached to his neck a large stone such as might be employed to drown a dog, and drawing the inanimate scholar by his feet to the brink of a neighbouring well, toppled him skilfully into its depths.

Subsequently he rejoined his imperial mistress whom he found refreshing herself with sips from a cup filled with the rose-essence of the Academicians.

"Undeniably," sighed she, "it is a pity that so delightful a young man must be suppressed, but he was inclined to be vain and would never have kept the secret of his good fortune."

And Li-Lien-Yn, agreeing, replied:

"In any case, what poet could aspire to a better end than that of being sacrificed on the altar of love?"

The Woman Who Commanded

CHAPTER NINETEEN

In order to calm her nerves which were slightly
overstimulated in consequence of her adventure with
the delightful young man, Tseu-Hi had resolved to
smoke a few pipes of opium.

An apostle of self-control, she rarely employed the
drug, which she regarded as a valuable remedy or a
detestable poison according to the manner in which
it was used.

But for the accursed English who opposed her on
commercial grounds, she would have forbidden the use
of opium throughout the Celestial Empire for the
majority of her subjects, whom she judged incapable
of distinguishing between use and abuse. But she
admitted of happy exceptions, among which she
naturally placed herself.

It was for this reason that on the morning following her amorous adventure, she invited Li-Lien-Yn to
lie down beside her upon the huge bed reserved for
this purpose, in order to prepare her pipes. In
doing so she conferred upon him a signal honour,
even though the Grand Eunuch had in some sort become the Prince Consort of the Empress.

Like his unfortunate predecessor Ngan-Te-Hai, he
insisted upon being addressed as "Lord of Nine

Thousand Years," thus demonstrating that, next to the Son of Heaven, he considered himself the most important person in the Celestial Empire.

Lying upon her side, her head supported by a finely woven cane pillow, Tseu-Hi watched with interest the Grand Eunuch's culinary operations.

Having selected a long silver needle, Li-Lien-Yn carefully rotated its point in the sticky brown drug that filled a small porcelain jar at his side. When a little ball had collected on the end of the needle, he skilfully moulded it with his taper fingers and set it to fry above the flame of a small lamp which stood on a tray containing an assortment of smoking accessories. The opium blistered and sizzled gently. Then Li-Lien-Yn, remoulding the pill, rolled it once again while still hot in the drug, so as to collect a second coat which would in its turn be fried.

He repeated this delicate operation several times, and, judging it to be completed, placed the meticulously prepared pellet in the bowl of a pipe. Remained only the final precaution of piercing it through in order to facilitate combustion.

Then Li-Lien-Yn, with profound respect, offered the pipe to his divine mistress.

Tseu-Hi received it with dignity. Grasping the thick bamboo in both hands, she voluptuously applied her lips to the ivory mouthpiece, and holding the partially reversed bowl over the lamp, inhaled deeply so as to ignite the drug.

The Woman Who Commanded

From the delicate nostrils of her aquiline nose, she expelled clouds of dense white smoke which floated above her imperial countenance.

A profound well-being possessed her and her nerves relaxed deliciously.

At the sixth pipe she became almost unconscious of her body. It seemed to her that her mind, divorced from matter, comprehended all things with extraordinary lucidity.

In a strange and far-away voice she murmured an ancient Buddhist maxim:

"How can men aspire to be happy? They are as goldfish swimming in a broken bowl from which the water is slowly draining away."

Then, with a smile, she added:

"They are all under sentence of death from the hour of their birth. What can they hope for except to survive a few years in the hearts of those who have loved them? Thus it is a blessing from Heaven to die in the full tide of love, having known neither sorrow nor disillusion."

She paused a moment in order to smoke her seventh pipe and resumed:

"That delightful young man was really much to be envied . . . and he was indeed an exquisite person. . . . Tell me, Li-Lien-Yn, do you know of others that would strike you as equally worthy?"

The Grand Eunuch replied with the utmost composure:

"To please Your Majesty, I would accomplish the impossible. . . . And in any case I have, I think, given irrefutable proof that I am no mere courtier when I assure Your Majesty that your beauty has not lost its youthful brilliance."

"Nevertheless the dusk must fall," sighed Tseu-Hi, "the most beautiful day can only end in night; but I am grateful to you for assisting me to make the most of this hour which to me seems the fairest of any because it is the last."

She concluded:

"And so you clearly understand . . . this very night I shall expect . . ."

She left her sentence unfinished: an agreeable languor was invading her brain, and closing her eyes she abandoned herself to a recuperative slumber. Slightly troubled, the Grand Eunuch lay beside her, watching the repose of this exquisite woman whose absolute authority could, for the merest whim, send any one of her innumerable subjects to precede her at the Yellow Fountains.

For himself he had very little anxiety, since his condition was such that he was unlikely to be involved in any amorous intrigue . . . and yet, somehow, he could not but regret the fact!

CHAPTER TWENTY

The Grand Eunuch had expended treasures of imagination in order to meet the ever more insatiable desires of his divine mistress; and still Tseu-Hi was dissatisfied both in flesh and in spirit. She was even becoming bored with these transitory experiences which palled with repetition.

And once more her thoughts turned to Yong-Lou whom she more decidedly than ever felt to be the one and only man to whom she would entirely respond.

Whereupon, overriding all vain formalities, she recalled him from his official exile by imperial decree, and very shortly the Grand Tartar Marshal of Chen-Si resumed command of the Manchu Guard at Peking as though nothing had occurred to interrupt his career.

In point of fact, quite apart from gratifying the dearest wish of her heart, the Empress did not regard it as a bad stroke of policy to have once more within immediate call a hero who enjoyed the absolute adoration of his troops. Li-Houng-Tchang, Viceroy of Petchili, was of course always at hand, ready to afford his benefactress the assistance of his modern army, but Yong-Lou and his Manchus offered yet greater security.

Five Hundred Million Men

Then came the memorable day when Yong-Lou, after seven long years of exile, set out for the Summer Palace, there to present to his omnipotent mistress his respectful homage together with his undying repentance for all that he had made her suffer.

Adorned as for a great ceremony, Tseu-Hi anxiously awaited the return of the faithless lover.

She had remained long before her copper mirror, gazing at her own features, asking herself with disagreeable misgivings whether she had not aged unduly during those intervening years.

By certain unmistakable signs she knew that her youth, till then so miraculously preserved, was at length about to take its departure. And she was haunted by the thought that very soon, love the divine would be for her aging body no more than a pitiable parody.

With what passionate ardour, therefore, did she, nearing the end of her youth's journey, aspire to those embraces which would be the last!

When Yong-Lou made his appearance she advanced to meet him with genuinely deep emotion, watching him closely and trying to read in his mind what impression she had made upon him after the lapse of so many years. But Yong-Lou, in obedience to custom, was preparing to execute before the Dowager Empress the genuflexions which were prescribed by tradition.

The Woman Who Commanded

With a sharp gesture Tseu-Hi stopped him, faltering in a low voice:

"Have you nothing left to offer me but respect?"

And her eyes were so unutterably desolate that Yong-Lou was profoundly moved, and sought in his turn to read in them whether she still loved him.

For several moments they stood thus gazing at each other in mutual interrogation.

Then suddenly, knowing themselves to be alone in the audience chamber of which the doors had been closed by Tseu-Hi's express command, they fell into one another's arms and clung together in a passionate embrace.

Completely calmed at last, Tseu-Hi murmured in gentle and melodious tones:

"For a woman, there is only one love that counts in her life, and that is the first one, which is also sincere, disinterested and durable! . . . She is indeed fortunate if, when she comes to die, that love is also the last!"

And tenderly she called to mind the happy bygone hours which seemed to live again before her eyes even as the Summer Palace had risen in glory from its ashes.

Five Hundred Million Men

CHAPTER TWENTY-ONE

The Empress Tseu-Hi was about to celebrate her sixtieth birthday. Despite the fact that she was very far from looking her age and that she had retained a quite amazingly seductive appearance, she thought it only correct to conform with time-honoured custom and to prepare extraordinary rejoicings in honour of the occasion.

For forty years she had virtually reigned over the Celestial Empire, ever since the glorious day upon which, as a simple concubine, she had borne to the Holy Man Hien-Foung that only heir who was destined to succeed his father as the Emperor Toung-Tche. On that day she had risen in one bound to supreme authority, and ever since then, whether under cover of the name of a witless and feeble Holy Man, or out in the open as acknowledged sovereign, she it was who had either inspired or drawn up every imperial decree, and had directed as she saw fit the strange policy of the Celestial Empire.

At this very hour, although she had for some years elected to live in retirement at the Summer Palace, she remained the Omnipotent Sovereign with right and power to dictate her commands when and how she chose.

The Woman Who Commanded

Whenever she momentarily quitted her residence and returned to preside at a particularly interesting meeting of the Grand Council in the Forbidden City, the Son of Heaven, the divine Kouang-Siu, came out to meet his illustrious aunt and prostrated himself before her in order to make it abundantly and officially clear that he had remained her humble and obedient servant.

It was therefore needful to give exceptional prominence to the celebrations connected with the sixtieth birthday of the "old buddha" as the people still affectionately termed her whom they venerated as their "sacred mother."

With this end in view, supplementary taxes were everywhere imposed and were gladly accepted and substantial levies were made upon all official salaries.

Very soon, several millions of gold taels had been amassed for the purpose of celebrating the event with unprecedented pomp.

On the road leading to the Summer Palace, triumphal arches were being constructed and sumptuous altars erected where litanies would be sung to the already beatified Tseu-Hi.

Marshal Yong-Lou who, together with the Grand Eunuch Li-Lien-Yn, was to figure in the forefront of the ceremony, was making grandiose preparations for the apotheosis of his divine mistress, while the Holy Man and his entire Court were getting ready to offer adequate homage to the venerable aunt who was so magnificently interring her youth.

Suddenly a terrible piece of news came to overcast the rejoicings. The "Japanese dwarfs" had sunk the *Kow-Shing,* an English ship transporting Chinese troops to Korea.

War was inevitable. Very soon, Tseu-Hi heard that her generals had been defeated at Ping-Yang, then at Port Arthur, while the entire fleet had been annihilated at Weï-Haï-Weï, of which the "dwarfs" had taken possession (1894).

It was utter and complete disaster.

Tseu-Hi was wounded to the very heart by the national mourning, and she hastened to countermand the orders for all the fêtes which had been arranged in her honour.

So Li-Houng-Tchang had deceived her in his affirmations that, once his troops were armed and equipped in the modern manner, they would be invincible! Utter disillusion now succeeded the rodomontades of the presumptuous Chinese!

Li-Houng-Tchang lost in a moment all influence with Tseu-Hi, who promptly caused him to be superseded.

It remained for a Manchu, the aged Prince Kuong, to profit by events and regain the foremost place in the government.

In a moment of ill-humour, ten years earlier, Tseu-Hi had held Prince Kuong responsible for the defeat of the Celestial Empire in the struggle against France over Tonkin.

She now realised that Li-Houng-Tchang had had no better success in keeping the Japanese out of Korea.

It was therefore not individuals that she must blame for the weakness of the Chinese armaments; the evil lay deeper and was perhaps irremediable, residing as it probably did in the fact that heterogeneous mercenaries enrolled under diverse flags could not be expected to possess the moral force which is one of the primary factors of success.

Tseu-Hi in recalling Prince Kuong made a tacit admission of this great truth.

Moreover, now that age was rendering her more thoughtful, she experienced a great pleasure at being once more surrounded by the members of her own family. Prince Kuong, brother to the Emperor Hien-Foung, therefore, became Councillor to the Throne, replacing his other brother, Prince Tchouen, who had died some three years previously.

Tseu-Hi, as of yore, wished to give the control of public affairs to a loyal and devoted Manchu in whom she could place unlimited trust.

She thus re-created the past and returned to the old conservative policy from which she had been suborned by Li-Houng-Tchang.

Moreover, Prince Kuong was a wise and experienced man who had formerly got Tseu-Hi out of more than one difficulty. Quite without ill-feeling and displaying a fine generosity of spirit, he resumed the post of which he had earlier been deprived and set to work immediately to strengthen the foundations of the Dragon's Throne which had been severely shaken by military reverses.

Meanwhile, Li-Houng-Tchang had gone to Japan to sign a hasty armistice. The wily old fox had succeeded in persuading Russia, Germany and France to intervene and exert pressure on Japan in order to prevent her from drawing full profit from her victories and from annexing Korea and the Manchu provinces.

Japan, therefore, had to be content with the large island of Formosa and to resign herself to establishing a mere protectorate over Korea; but she claimed and secured a heavy war indemnity. As a consequence of this peace, which was concluded at Shimonoseki, the great powers also demanded payment for their efforts on behalf of China.

Germany annexed Kiao-Tcheou and Russia settled into that same Port Arthur which she had compelled Japan to return to China. Japan, moreover, never forgave the perfidy of Russia. Ten years later she was to reconquer Port Arthur after a savage war (1904-1905).

France, with more discretion, did not hold on to Chéfou which had been assigned to her opposite Port Arthur, but she nevertheless claimed the territory of

Kouang-Tcheou-Wang, near Tonkin, which she has kept to this day.

As for England, not to be left out in the cold by the other great powers, she firmly established herself at Weï-Haï-Weï.

CHAPTER TWENTY-TWO

After the disasters of the Chino-Japanese War, Tseu-Hi, much saddened but not discouraged, had once more retired to the Summer Palace, leaving Prince Kuong to his former task of presiding at the meetings of the Grand Council and drawing up the more important decrees.

He also directed the Tsoung-Li-Yamen, a species of Foreign Office which had been established with a view to communicating with Barbarian Ministers without its being necessary to admit them to the Forbidden City.

Marshal Yong-Lou had been appointed Viceroy of Petchili and had his official residence at Tien-Tsin, which, however, did not prevent him from paying frequent visits to Tseu-Hi in order to seek her advice.

Finally, the Empress Dowager had still a faithful ally near the Holy Man Kouang-Siu, in the person of the Empress Consort, her niece Long-You, the daughter of her brother Duke Kouei.

Believing herself therefore to be secure from any surprise, Tseu-Hi employed the leisure of her semi-retirement in ardent pursuit of the arts of painting and literature. She was exceedingly skilful with her brush, and failing other eminence might well have acquired renown as a painter or a poetess.

She was also of an extreme erudition, and could have given points to any specialist on earth regarding the ancient history of China.

Then, again, she had so pronounced a passion for the stage that not only did she frequently attend theatrical performances, but she did not disdain occasionally to interpret a principal part in the drama in partnership with the Grand Eunuch Li-Lien-Yn.

It must be admitted that these performances did some damage to her reputation and did not fail to shock the official Censors; but Tseu-Hi had long been accustomed to ignore the conventional criticisms of these dotards.

Having reigned unchallenged for nearly half a century it never even entered her head that anyone could question the authority given her from Above. And yet, utterly unknown to her, a formidable intrigue was being brewed against her.

Secretly, without the knowledge of his wife, Long-You, the Son of Heaven was conspiring against his venerable aunt Tseu-Hi with a view to shaking off her intolerable yoke.

In 1891 he had lost his father, Prince Tchouen, who had married Tseu-Hi's sister, and in 1896 he had endured the further sorrow of seeing his mother ascend the Dragon's Chariot.

An orphan now, his hatred of Tseu-Hi was no

longer restrained by a fear of distressing his own parents and he fully intended at length to demonstrate a measure of self-sufficiency.

In his rebellious intentions he was supported by Weng-Toung-Ho, his former tutor, who had brought him up with the aid of the deceased Empress Tseu-Ngan.

Weng-Toung-Ho, who had never left the Holy Man Kouang-Siu since that Sovereign's earliest infancy, felt for his former pupil a respectful but deep affection which His Majesty returned to him with interest.

It was thus that Kouang-Siu had protected Weng-Toung-Ho from the vengeance of Yong-Lou who had found it hard to forgive him his blunder of having surprised him in the company of Tseu-Ngan's maid of honour. The Holy Man had further obtained for his favourite a place on the Grand Council where he surreptitiously advanced views opposed to those of Tseu-Hi.

In any case, Weng-Toung-Ho remained the friend and confidential secretary of Kouang-Siu. Of purely Chinese extraction and born in the province of Kiang-Sou, Weng-Toung-Ho in his innermost soul hated the official domination by the Manchu race which was so beloved of the Empress Tseu-Hi; on the other hand, he firmly believed that the salvation of China could only be accomplished by making a clean sweep of the past.

The Woman Who Commanded

Curiously enough, he had contrived to impose his entirely revolutionary ideas upon the Son of Heaven Himself, who was, for that matter, ready enough for any rebellion that would release him from the tyranny of Tseu-Hi.

In order to help forward his plans, Weng-Toung-Ho had introduced into the Holy Man's household a celebrated Southern agitator named Kang-Yeou-Wei, who was equally opposed to the Manchus and the conservative party.

Little by little, Kang-Yeou-Wei, who was of exceptional intelligence and extremely learned, acquired a preponderating influence over the mind of the unfortunate Holy Man, who, if the truth must be told, had only one desire: to be rid, in one way or another, of his terrible aunt. For she now imposed upon Kouang-Siu every kind of painful humiliation, forcing him, when he visited her at the Summer Palace, to kneel before her door under the jeering gaze of the eunuchs, until such time as she might deign to receive him.

The first skirmishes soon took place between the South-Chinese party which was secretly revolutionary and at any rate openly advocated reform, and the Northern or Manchu party which remained fiercely conservative.

Weng-Toung-Ho, protected by the Son of Heaven, obtained some initial successes, as, for instance, the suppression of the antiquated classical examinations,

till then deemed indispensable preliminaries to a title
or office.

But Tseu-Hi retaliated by promptly evicting
Weng-Toung-Ho, who was forced to retire to his
native province.

At which juncture occurred the regrettable death
of Prince Kuong, who had acted as a mediating ele-
ment between the two parties and who, while retaining over both a great and legitimate influence, had
been the only person capable of repressing their
conflicts or of finding a moderate alternative solution.

With his death the political situation rapidly gained
impetus.

Kouang-Siu, advised by Kang-Yeou-Wei, who had
replaced Weng-Toung-Ho in his household, resolved
to accomplish a smashing coup-d'état (1898).

With this end in view, he summoned to his side
Youan-Chi-Kai who, formerly secretary to Li-Houng-
Tchang in Korea, had now replaced his master as
commander in chief of the modernised army. First
of all, the Son of Heaven reminded Youan-Chi-Kai
of his expressed desire to support a policy of reform,
then he asked him whether, in case of need, he could
depend upon his loyal assistance.

Without the slightest hesitation, Youan-Chi-Kai
took a solemn oath to uphold His Majesty's sacred
cause even to the death.

But on leaving the Imperial Presence, he was
swiftly sent for by the Empress Dowager, who made

short work of extracting from him a full confession and of winning him as an adherent to her own party.

After which manœuvre, Tseu-Hi, justly incensed at what had come to pass, descended upon her nephew with whom, as was her custom, she made a truly terrific scene, exacting the immediate arrest of Kang-Yeou-Wei.

Kouang-Siu feigned submission, but he surreptitiously sent a eunuch to warn Kang-Yeou-Wei of the danger that menaced him, and the latter fled in haste and made his escape to Japan where for many years he continued to conspire indefatigably against the Manchus.

Tseu-Hi was profoundly irritated by the escape of her prey, but, on the other hand, she decided that all danger was averted and that the Son of Heaven was never again likely to raise his head.

She therefore returned to the Summer Palace and calmly resumed her favourite occupations in company with the Grand Eunuch.

But for the first time in her life she had lacked intuition, for Kouang-Siu, exasperated by that culminating scene of violence, had firmly resolved at any cost to throw off a yoke that was quite intolerable and contrary to his dignity.

The very next day he again sent for Youan-Chi-Kai who once more assured him of his unqualified devotion.

Whereupon, proudly, and, as it turned out, for the

last time, ascending the Dragon's Throne, Kouang-
Siu promulgated a succession of decrees relating to
fundamental reforms in army and administration;
then, surrounded by his intimates and fellow conspirators against the Empress' party, he commanded
Youan-Chi-Kai to go immediately to Tien-Tsin and
there to arrest and behead Marshal Yong-Lou.
Youan-Chi-Kai was himself to succeed the Marshal
as viceroy of Petchili, and, assuming command of
the troops, was to march to the Summer Palace
where he was to arrest the Empress Tseu-Hi and
throw her into the prison in which she would spend
her remaining days, while the Grand Eunuch and
all her other adherents were to be summarily executed.

Youan-Chi-Kai promised faithfully to execute His
Majesty's orders which were accompanied by an ar-
row, symbolical of transmitted imperial authority.

The plot being thus minutely laid, Kouang-Siu
closed the audience and in order to avoid arousing
Tseu-Hi's suspicions, politely escorted her to the
Temple of Silk where she wished, in accordance with
an ancient custom, to spin the first cocoon of the
season. Never had the Emperor been so deferential;
he performed for his aunt's benefit the three genuflexions and the nine prostrations with the greatest
outward humility, reflecting with inward rapture that
these were the last antics which he would ever
execute before his venerable relation.

Meanwhile Youan-Chi-Kai, having made great

diligence, had arrived at Tien-Tsin before the Hour of the Sheep. He immediately made his way to the Yamen of Marshal Yong-Lou, exactly as he had promised the Holy Man.

Yong-Lou was in no wise surprised to receive an unexpected visit from Youan-Chi-Kai, since these two great men were "brothers"; that is to say, they had taken the oath of brotherhood in the secret society to which they both belonged.

Youan-Chi-Kai inquired gravely:

"Are you still my brother?"

"And shall be until death, come what may," replied Yong-Lou.

"In that case," resumed Youan-Chi-Kai, "I will myself act as a brother."

Whereupon he quickly informed Yong-Lou of the exact situation, omitting not the smallest detail.

The Marshal was not a man to waste time in surprise even at such unexpected news. He was, however, astonished that Tseu-Hi, usually so shrewd, had not suspected this last intrigue. But the time had not yet come for such speculations; the important thing was to warn her without further delay.

And Yong-Lou, hastily leaving his Yamen, started for Peking which he reached that same evening.

With the utmost celerity he made his way to the Violet Town where Tseu-Hi was spending the night after having accomplished her pilgrimage to the Temple of Silk; regardless of etiquette, he strode into the Palace by the Lake, where Tseu-Hi was preparing to go to bed.

Scandalised by such a breach of etiquette, Tseu-Hi was about to express her displeasure in no mild terms, when Yong-Lou, wasting no time in excuses, started to explain the motive of his intrusion.

As soon as Tseu-Hi had grasped the situation, she warmly thanked Yong-Lou for the promptitude with which he had come to her aid, and begged him to assist her in parrying the stroke aimed at her by Kouang-Siu.

Having reflected for some moments, she determined that the first step was to summon all the leaders of the conservative party in consultation.

Yong-Lou set out at once to seek them and was fortunately able to bring them all to the Palace by the Lake before the Hour of the Tiger.

They included the Princes of the Blood who had remained loyal to the Empress; most of the members of the Grand Council and the high officials, and also the Ministers whom Kouang-Siu had recently superseded and who were particularly glad of an opportunity for immediate revenge.

All these illustrious individuals threw themselves devoutly at the feet of their "old buddha," and, having once more renewed their vows of undying loyalty, they implored her openly to resume the Supreme Authority, to take her seat upon the Dragon's Throne, dispossessing for ever the Son of Heaven who was a traitor to his Manchu blood and to all dynastic traditions.

Tseu-Hi willingly allowed herself to be persuaded of the necessity for again appearing, more powerful and more autocratic than ever, upon the public stage; in order to demonstrate that she had lost none of her former energy, she arranged for the arrest at dawn of her recalcitrant nephew and for his incarceration under strict guard in a lonely pavilion situated in the midst of the Southern lake in the Imperial Park. Later on, after mature consideration, his ultimate fate would be determined. All those present heartily approved this prompt decision, and each one, having made his obeisance to the "old buddha," withdrew to the special duty that had been assigned to him.

Yong-Lou himself hastened to replace the guards of the Forbidden City by loyal Manchu soldiers, then, reassured on that point, he returned to Tien-Tsin in order to resume his post as Governor of Petchili and to give the necessary orders which would ensure universal acceptance of the Empress' coup d'état.

As for the Grand Eunuch, he was equally diligent in mobilising the cohorts of castrates who were to be held ready for action inside the Violet Town.

At dawn of day, the Holy Man, Kouang-Siu, who was far from suspecting the treachery of Youan-Chi-Kai, came calmly forth from the Chamber of the Sacred Repose and proceeded to the Temple of An-

cestors, there to pray before the tablets of his forebears, for their favourable support in the blow he
was to strike on that day against the Empress
Dowager.

Suddenly, before he had time to collect himself,
he was surrounded by Yong-Lou's soldiers and Li-
Lien-Yn's eunuchs, while his small suite hastily made
its escape.

A few moments later he was on his way under
armed escort to the Pavilion on the Terrace of the
Ocean, where he was placed in the closest confinement like a dangerous criminal.

By way of consolation the Grand Eunuch merely
informed him with a sarcastic smile that he would
shortly be honoured by a visit from the Empress
Dowager who was anxious to obtain from him some
explanation regarding his recent activities.

The Woman Who Commanded

As soon as Tseu-Hi learnt that Kouang-Siu had been arrested and confined under strict guard on the Island of the Terrace of the Ocean, she hastened without delay, and with incredible presence of mind, to take all necessary dispositions.

A few hours earlier she had expected to pass a peaceful night in the Violet Town prior to returning on the morrow to the Summer Palace and there resuming all her favourite occupations; instead of which she had suddenly accomplished a prodigious coup d'état which had had to be engineered at a moment's notice.

But nothing in the world could shake her colossal self-confidence, just as the most shattering emotions left her health and clear-sightedness unaltered.

Resuming immediate authority, she gave orders for the arrest and execution of all those who had in any way been involved in the Kouang-Siu conspiracy.

Within a few moments, heads had already begun to fall.

Meanwhile, in full Grand Council, Tseu-Hi accorded herself permission to ascend the Dragon's Throne, thus demonstrating that she intended henceforth to govern as an absolute unaided autocrat, discarding even a fictional figurehead, such as had

266

always previously existed in the person of the Son of Heaven.

Finally, she then and there revoked all the recent imperial decrees in favour of reform and drew up a proclamation re-establishing throughout the country the old order of things, notably in the matter of the examinations which were to resume their earlier classical form.

Thunderous acclamations saluted her words; had not ritual tradition forbidden it, she would have been carried in triumph!

And Tseu-Hi was able to assure herself that never had her fascination been so great.

Deeply gratified, she made her way, accompanied only by the Grand Eunuch, to the Terrace of the Ocean.

Since dawn the trembling Kouang-Siu had awaited his aunt's visit.

The interview was a tragedy. Tseu-Hi, her nerves thoroughly on edge, opened it with violent and furious invectives.

"And so," she exclaimed, "you have had the presumption and the incredible stupidity to plot against me, as though you really thought yourself capable of success. . . . Are you unaware that if you are Son of Heaven, it is simply and solely because I made you so? . . . You have never been anything but a pitiable puppet, and many a time have the Manchus been so ashamed to see you occupy the Dragon's

Throne that they have begged of me to depose you and to take your place. . . . Out of respect for traditions and in remembrance of your father, Tchouen, and of your mother who was my beloved sister, I have so far been over-generous to you . . . but I have lived to repent of my generosity, and to see you ignominiously betray your race by plotting with Southern revolutionaries who seek only to overthrow the Empire and sow anarchy and ruin throughout all China. . . .

"A thousand times you have deserved to be crushed like a venomous snake . . . and if, for the moment, I spare your life, it is only for reasons of state and in order to avoid unnecessary scandal. . . .

"I shall merely await the day when I shall consider it wise to suppress you altogether . . . but from now onward, you are nothing, not even a man. . . . I condemn you to perpetual imprisonment and to the silence of the tomb . . . moreover, if ever you dare to commit the smallest indiscretion, I will have you whipped by my eunuchs like a common urchin, till the blood flows! . . ."

And in order to demonstrate that this was no mere empty threat, Tseu-Hi actually belaboured with the handle of her fan the wretched Kouang-Siu who had crumpled up in a heap at her feet.

Never before had she flown into so terrible a rage; the paper windows of the pavilion positively shook at the vibrations of her furious voice, while the Grand Eunuch contemplated with visible satisfaction the humiliation of the malevolent Holy Man who had planned his execution.

Quitting the pavilion, Tseu-Hi had a further interview with Long-You, daughter of her brother, Duke Kouei. It was agreed between the two Empresses that they alone, apart from the eunuch in attendance, should have access to Kouang-Siu's prison.

The Empress Consort had faithfully spied upon the Holy Man on behalf of her aunt. It was not her fault that she had been unable to warn Tseu-Hi of the impending plot, for Kouang-Siu, who loathed her, had banished her from his presence for several successive moons. And now Long-You would be in a position to take a sensational revenge and to humiliate and torture her wretched husband to her heart's content.

The Empress Dowager knew what she was about when she placed the fallen Son of Heaven in the custody of his former wife. But she also took care to sequestrate Kouang-Siu's favourite concubine, who answered to the pleasant name of Miss Pearl-of-Great-Price. With refined cruelty the Empress Consort was selected to convey to Kouang-Siu the cheering tidings that Miss Pearl-of-Great-Price would share his incarceration and was to hold herself in readiness to accompany him upon the long journey to the Yellow Fountains. This was a last and delicate attention on the part of his venerable aunt.

The Woman Who Commanded

CHAPTER TWENTY-FOUR

From the day of his sequestration on the Island of the Terrace of the Ocean, Kouang-Siu ceased to be Son of Heaven in anything but name. He saw no one but Tseu-Hi and the Empress Consort who only spoke to him in order to insult him; he languished in intolerable boredom while awaiting the hour of death which he knew could not be long delayed.

Several moons passed without his leaving his pavilion, save on rare occasions when custom prescribed his presence at some ceremony or when he went under adequate guard to pray before certain altars or to perform ancestral worship. But as soon as the ceremony was concluded he was hurried back to his prison without being permitted to utter a single word.

Meanwhile Tseu-Hi had started to publish a series of decrees in which she announced the steadily increasing ill-health of the Son of Heaven; a measure which was essential if public opinion was to be prepared for the imminent removal of Kouang-Siu to a better world.

With an eye to outward seemliness she even commanded the presence in Peking of the most celebrated physicians of the entire Celestial Empire; but since

270

these experts, as we have already said, were only permitted to approach a Holy Man on their knees, and were forbidden even for a moment to raise their heads in order to look at the patient, diagnosis was a decidedly difficult matter.

They again prescribed a few harmless remedies at a venture, recommended rest and much good food, and withdrew, still on all fours, in testimony of their profound respect for the dynasty.

After this remarkable consultation Tseu-Hi issued a bulletin to the effect that Kouang-Siu was very ill indeed and could not be expected to survive more than a few days.

It was at this juncture that the representatives of foreign powers, influenced either by common humanity or by a dignified desire to dissociate their governments from any complicity in so sinister a farce, officially informed Tseu-Hi, via the medium of the Tsoung-Li-Yamen, that the Holy Man, Kouang-Siu's premature ascension of the Dragon's Chariot would be viewed with extreme disfavour.

The Empress Dowager was extremely annoyed by such an intrusion into her private affairs, but on being advised by her faithful Yong-Lou that it would be prudent to temporise, she postponed the decree which was to have informed the populace that the Holy Man was sinking; on the contrary, to the great astonishment, not only of his subjects in general but especially of the Court officials who had been hourly expecting his demise, the Son of Heaven took a turn for the better and gradually returned to perfect health.

Not that Tseu-Hi had any intention of forgiving Kouang-Siu; if she had unwillingly consented to postpone his execution, she was none the less firmly determined to depose him.

She had even held a grand family council for the purpose of announcing that the next Emperor would be Pou-Tsiun, son of Prince Touan, a direct descendant in the male line from the Emperor Tao-Kouang.

This choice was accepted with the greater enthusiasm, in that Prince Touan symbolised both the ancient conservative spirit and the most violent xenophobia.

It was by no means only at Court that the sea-devils were hated. For several years a violent animosity against anything foreign had been spreading throughout all classes of the population of the Celestial Empire.

The paleface Barbarians and the "Japanese dwarfs" made little effort to conceal their intention of treating China as a conquered country, and their diplomatists were already engaged in cutting her up into various "zones of influence."

The Germans, under pretext of avenging the murder of two missionaries, had lately seized the vast territory round Kiao-Tcheou, and were claiming a large base for future development, as the English had already done at Hong-Kong and at Weï-Haï-Weï, the Russians at Port Arthur, the Japanese at Formosa and the French at Kouan-Tcheou-Wan.

These districts had become regular conquests, quite unlike the ordinary mercantile concessions at Tien-Tsin, Shanghai, Han-Keou, Canton and other open ports. Moreover, the foreigners under various pretexts were beginning to exact concessions of mines and railways while biding their time for the opportunity of grabbing further riches.

Tseu-Hi was ignorant of no detail regarding this invasion of her Empire by the foreigners whom she had so savagely hated ever since the burning of the Summer Palace and the flight to Jehol. In unison with her entire people she was consumed with fury and with one all-pervading desire: that of evicting the foreigners from China. Word to this effect had gone forth from the Court even unto the uttermost parts of the Empire.

Already there was rioting against the foreigner wherever he made his appearance; Christian institutions were attacked; missionaries were pursued and massacred; merchandise from abroad was boycotted or destroyed.

But Tseu-Hi still hesitated to initiate hostilities against the entire universe. Since the last war with Japan, she no longer had any illusions regarding the practical efficiency of her troops, despite the efforts which she had made to augment their value as a fighting unit. Youan-Chi-Kai had in fact succeeded in concentrating at Petchili a strongly organised modern army, while Chang-Chi-Toung, Viceroy of the two Hous, was engaged, with the assistance of German instructors, in forging an up-to-date force at Ou-Tchang and was establishing at Hanyang, on the Yang-Tse-Kiang, a formidable arsenal, constructed under the supervision of European engineers.

But Tseu-Hi's superior intelligence had realised that it does not suffice to have well-trained and well-equipped troops, it is also necessary to be backed by the entire nation, ready to make every sacrifice and to endure to the end. It was this indispensable factor that had failed her in all her previous quarrels with the Barbarians.

She would, therefore, have continued to temporise, had not Prince Touan affirmed that he could guarantee to rouse the entire population in an irresistible movement against the foreigner, and had not his contention been passionately supported by the other Princes of the Blood and by the members of the Grand Council, led by the celebrated reactionary minister, Kang-Hi.

As a matter of fact, the Court viewed with approval the arising throughout China of local militia that would later combine to form a nation in arms. This movement was particularly active in the Northern Provinces, under the influence of a strange sect whose adherents were christened "Boxers" by the Europeans because of their Chinese name of "The Fists of the Plum Blossom."

These fanatics, whose motto was: "Protection for the Dynasty and extermination of all foreigners," claimed to be invulnerable and imposed this naïve belief upon the credulous masses by means of extravagant jugglery. Prince Touan, who regarded them as likely to prove useful, feigned to be convinced by their sorceries and encouraged their propaganda. Very soon, large bands of "Boxers" invaded towns and country, sowing terror as they went and committing every kind of imposition.

Suspicious and fully aware of the civil danger presented by these cohorts of armed bandits, Tseu-Hi refused to support them openly, but, on the other hand, she was unwilling to oppose a body which represented a valuable asset in her struggle against the foreigners.

Meanwhile Yong-Lou, whom she had appointed as a member of the Grand Council and who in addition to being Governor of Petchili was now also commander-in-chief of all the Northern Armies, Grand Secretary and thus the highest dignitary in the Empire, was entirely in favour of temporisation and considered it as pure folly to count principally on the prestige and invulnerability of the Boxers for success against the Europeans and Japanese.

Tseu-Hi, moreover, retained her entire confidence

in Yong-Lou and had no intention of disregarding his advice, and there resulted a situation in which, for the first time in her life, she hesitated as to her course of action. She loathed the foreigners and would have been only too happy to see them utterly stamped out; on the other hand, she was doubtful of the final accomplishment of so desirable an end and wished to reserve a niche in public opinion in case of disaster. Finally, she even feared that the Boxers, should they become triumphant, might develop into a peril that would prove difficult of repression.

Nevertheless, on the day when she had the effrontery to present to the unhappy and stupefied Kouang-Siu his imminent successor, she accomplished a highly significant gesture. It was practically a declaration of war to proclaim as future Holy Man a son of Prince Touan who was not only the revered chief of the anti-foreign party, but also the inspiration of the "Boxer" movement. No one was under any illusions as to the true meaning of this proceeding, least of all the foreigners.

The ministers of the various powers immediately informed their respective governments and urgently asked for armed assistance.

Tseu-Hi vainly endeavoured to throw dust in their eyes by inviting the foreign ladies to a grand reception at which she exerted for their benefit every possible seduction; the wily smile of the "old buddha" did not suffice to allay the well-founded fears of the legations respecting their personal safety.

Events, moreover, moved quickly. News arrived of the ghastly massacre in the province of Chen-Si of some sixty Catholic and Protestant missionaries; then came word of the attack near Pao-Ting-Fou upon the Franco-Belgian mission schools on the Hang-Keou-Peking line, from which, however, most of the staff were able to accomplish a three days' fighting retreat, falling back upon the Tien-Tsin concession.

From that moment the final struggle became a foregone conclusion; and Tseu-Hi, in order to avoid being over-ridden by Prince Touan's party, was compelled to throw in her lot with them, despite the more temperate warnings of Marshal Yong-Lou.

Meanwhile the foreign ministers, not unnaturally anxious, had brought five hundred reinforcements from Tien-Tsin for the protection of the legations. They were only just in time, for on the following day the "Boxers" surrounded the quarter and the siege began. They were commanded not only by Prince Touan, but also by Prince Tchouang and Duke Lan, who were equally violent in their anti-foreign mania.

The celebrated chief, Toung-Fou-Sian, who had come from the distant province of Kiang-Sou with a band of savage Mussulman fanatics, also joined the party (1900).

But Marshal Yong-Lou, who considered this attack

contrary to international rights and harmful to the prestige of China, refused to allow his loyal Manchus to take any part in it and withheld his powerful artillery which would have made short work of the extemporary fortifications hastily erected by the defenders of the legations.

There existed thus in the Forbidden City two diametrically opposed parties: On the one hand, the Princes Tchouang and Touan, Duke Lan and other members of the Grand Council, such as Kang-Hi and Tchao-Chou-Kiao, desired the immediate extermination of all foreigners, regardless of age, sex or occupation; on the other hand, Marshal Yong-Lou, Prince King and the Chinese Sin-King-Tcheng and Youen-Tchang, while equally loathing the foreigners, held it folly to declare war upon the entire world by an indiscriminate massacre of all the representatives of foreign powers.

As for old Prince Li, the doyen of the Grand Council, he was chiefly engaged in assuring the safety of his personal possessions.

The Empress, placed as she was between two rival factions, each of which in turn advanced arguments and even threats, found herself in a very difficult situation. For this reason she would at one moment permit the Princes Tchouang and Touan, the wily Duke Lan and the brutal Toung-Fou-Sian to lead their hordes to the attack of the legations; an hour later, falling once more under the restraining influence of Yong-Lou, she would present her compliments to the foreign ministers, expressing her deep regret at the unruliness of the rioters, and assuring them of the efforts which she was making to protect the legations. She would, in point of fact, stop the firing and furnish fresh provisions to the besieged; but on the following day she would abandon the foreign ministers to their unhappy lot.

This behaviour of the Empress, which at first appeared inexplicable to the foreigners, was, in her own view, both wise and logical. No one would have been better pleased than she, had the "Boxers" and Toung-Fou-Sian's partisans succeeded in sacking the entire quarter of the legations, situated as it was in insolent proximity to the Forbidden City.

But she prudently refrained from permitting the intervention of regular troops, thus reserving for herself the perfidious excuse of having been forcibly overridden by agitators whom she officially repudiated while affording them secret support. She was, moreover, much too intelligent and too level-headed to believe in the occult powers of the "Boxers" or in their invulnerability against firearms, and she quite enormously mistrusted these fanatics whom she believed to be as capable of assassinating her imperial self as of massacring the foreign ministers.

She had good reason for her belief, for there came a fine afternoon on which a band of "Boxers," led by Prince Touan, forced their way into the Forbidden City in order to demand the head of the unhappy Holy Man, Kouang-Siu, whom they accused of conspiring with the foreigners. The real fact of the matter was that Prince Touan, whose son Pou-Tsiun had been officially proclaimed heir-presumptive, desired to see his son immediately replace Kouang-Siu on the Dragon's Throne. But Tseu-Hi did not relish having her hand forced; she did not intend to suppress Kouang-Siu until the correct moment, namely, until she had nothing to fear from the foreign powers.

Deeply incensed against Prince Touan, she bravely faced the rioters, barring their advance with such proud determination that the "Boxers" hesitated long enough to allow Yong-Lou's Manchus to fly to the rescue of their "old buddha."

Whereupon Tseu-Hi, with prompt decision, had the intruders immediately beheaded before her eyes, thereby affording herself an irrefutable proof that they were neither invulnerable nor invincible. She further informed Prince Touan that he was deprived of his pension and that any renewal of presumption on his part would deprive his son of his position as heir-presumptive to the Throne.

Prince Touan accepted the reproof and this erstwhile arrogant man threw himself humbly at the feet of the woman who had once more proved herself braver and more determined than any Manchu warrior.

Five Hundred Million Men

But from that time onwards Tseu-Hi hated him silently and sought only a favourable opportunity to be rid of him.

Meanwhile, her spirits rose and fell according to the news received from Yu-Lo, the new viceroy of Petchili, who was engaged in opposing the foreign invasion. The Barbarians had experienced some difficulty in gaining possession of the Forts of Ta-Kou, which protected the mouth of the Peï-Ho, for the cruisers, owing to shallow water, were unable to come within range and only the gunboats had opened fire. A lucky shot, however, from the French gunboat *Lion* exploded the magazine of one of the Chinese forts. This was the beginning of the end, and soon, with considerable losses, the expeditionary force contrived to land. But the campaign was by no means as simple as the foreigners had at first imagined.

The Chinese army of Petchili, trained successively by Li-Houng-Tchang and Youan-Chi-Kai, was of a temper quite unsuspected by the Europeans.

A first column, sent to the rescue of the legations by Lord Seymour, suffered a shattering reverse and was compelled to fall back upon the Tien-Tsin concessions which were in their turn vigorously attacked.

The fighting was particularly hot in the neighbourhood of the railway station where the French, sheltered behind barricades of salt, which had recently been unloaded, had great difficulty in repulsing the Chinese attack.

The Woman Who Commanded

It became necessary to await reinforcements, and it was not till August that a new column, under the command of the German general Von Waldersee, was able to start for Peking. After a series of warm engagements, it contrived to reach the walls of the capital.

The beaten Chinese army made no effort to pull itself together. Its demoralised mercenaries scattered in every direction, deaf to the expostulations of their chiefs, and Yu-Lo, viceroy of Petchili, blew out his brains in despair, after communicating to Tseu-Hi the news of the disaster.

After the repulse of Seymour's column, the Empress had tolerated the enaction of abominable scenes even at the very doors of her palace.

All the Christians in the Tartar Town had been massacred by the "Boxers," the French schools had been sacked and every house belonging to persons suspected of alien sympathies was burned to the ground.

Prince Tchouang had officially placed a price upon the head of every foreigner, giving command to spare neither man, woman nor child. An unfortunate English teacher, Mr. James, had been captured and cruelly tortured. His head, placed in a cage, adorned the chief entrance to the Forbidden City. Finally, gravest of all offences, the Chancellor of the Japanese Legation, Mr. Lugi-Yama, had been assassinated by the "Boxers," and soon afterwards the German

Minister himself, Baron von Ketteler, was shot in his chair on his way to the Tsoung-Li-Yamen to attend a parley with the Chinese Government.

Prince Touan actually wished to expose his head like that of Mr. James, but Yong-Lou and Prince King, already desperately distressed at the thought of the consequences of such a murder, utterly vetoed the suggestion.

Yong-Lou offered personally with the Manchu Guard to escort the foreign ministers to Tien-Tsin, but these latter hesitated, fearing an ambush, and moreover the "Boxers" and Toung-Fou-Sian's Mahometans barred their exit from the legations.

Toung-Fou-Sian even bribed a soldier to kill Yong-Lou, but the Marshal was so beloved by his men that the proposed assassin went immediately to warn his chief of the danger to which he was exposed.

In the meantime Tseu-Hi's fears of foreign vengeance were increased by the fact that the German Emperor, William II, outraged by the murder of his minister, Baron von Ketteler, was eloquently denouncing the "Yellow Peril" and preaching an international crusade against an empire which had placed itself beyond human sympathy by its contempt for all civilised restrictions.

There came an evening when the Empress learned that the "Japanese dwarfs," followed by the French and soon to be joined by the Germans, were about to attack the Tartar Town, while the English had already occupied the Temple of Heaven at the entrance to the Forbidden City. There was no time for hesitation; only an immediate flight could save her from the vengeance of the Barbarians.

Having slept but little, Tseu-Hi rose at the Hour of the Tiger and rapidly assumed the costume of an ordinary peasant which would save her from recognition by the Barbarians in the event of pursuit; she then left her palace and made her way to a lonely courtyard of the Forbidden City where she was awaited by a number of mule carts.

Shepherded by the eunuchs, the concubines clustered in a panic-stricken flock, while in another corner, the Holy Man, Kouang-Siu, half-awake and completely torpid, awaited the arrival of the "Sacred Mother."

The sound of cannon was borne on the night air from the legations, and stray projectiles whistled past; the Japanese were preparing to enter the Tartar Town.

To the west of the Forbidden City the shouts of the "Boxers" were clearly audible as they attempted a final assault on the Peï-Tang. In the cathedral and the neighbouring buildings, which had been transformed into forts, Monseigneur Flavier withstood an epic siege by fanatics bent upon the murder of all the Christian refugees in his mission. He had with him only forty French sailors and ten Italians commanded by Midshipman Henry.

284

Five Hundred Million Men

. This handful of heroes had succeeded in holding their own for several weeks against the hordes of Prince Tchouang and Toung-Fou-Sian. Outnumbered by a hundred to one, their achievement was prodigious. On that last evening there were barely a dozen left alive, all of them wounded; the others, including Midshipman Henry, had been killed.

But Monseigneur Flavier who, by some amazing fortune had remained unscathed, was performing miracles. At the head of his Christians, armed with anything they had been able to get hold of, he hurled back with his own hands the attacking devils.

He was a gigantic being with fierce eyes, a great hooked nose and an imposing grey beard. His voice was a roar and his muscles of steel served him well.

This amazing paladin struck real terror to the hearts of the superstitious "Boxers"; they saw in him the Great Foreign Devil in person and his appearance in battle sowed a strange panic among his assailants.

. Tseu-Hi was familiar with this terrible representative of the Western God and she felt a deep uneasiness at the knowledge that he was still alive and in such close proximity to her person. In a few hours he would probably be rescued by the victorious foreigners. And what might he not do to revenge himself? She already visualised him on her tracks, in which conception she strangely mistook the character of this individual, who emerging victorious from

285

the desperate struggle, was as ardent in pillage as he had been in the fight. With no desire to satisfy useless animosities, he concentrated upon the practical determination to extort from the enemy funds wherewith to restore his ruined mission, a determination which was certainly justifiable.

It was indeed a sinister day that dawned for the Empress. The sun was beginning to flush the east above the curved roofs. Distant cries, mingled with the rattle of artillery, incessantly smote the ear, while within the Forbidden City a deathly silence hovered over the deserted palaces.

Tense with repressed emotions, Tseu-Hi was about to give the order for departure, when she was interrupted by a small, shrill voice.

It was Kouang-Siu's favourite concubine, Miss Pearl-of-Great-Price, who, destined originally to accompany her Lord on his journey to the Yellow Fountains, was permitting herself, after two years of imprisonment, to express an opinion regarding the advisability of flight for the Holy Man whom she was once more privileged to behold.

This unexpected audacity set a climax to the exasperation of the already irritated Empress. Addressing the Grand Eunuch who stood near her, she commanded him then and there to silence for ever this impudent hussy, and Li-Lien-Yn hastened to obey. With the aid of another eunuch, he dragged Miss Pearl-of-Great-Price to a large well in the

corner of the courtyard and hurled her head foremost
into its depths.

Kouang-Siu stood by, a despairing witness of the
summary execution of the only woman he had ever
loved; he was almost in a swooning condition.

But Tseu-Hi, judging the moment inopportune for
any display of futile sentimentality, hustled the Son
of Heaven into the cart which awaited him, begging
him to keep the hood well extended over his august
countenance, in order to avoid a recognition that
might have the gravest consequence for the convoy.

Having also seen to the safe disposal of Pou-Tsiun,
the heir presumptive, in another cart, she finally gave
the signal for departure.

A few hours later, despite the delays occasioned
by the crowds of fugitives who were leaving the Tartar Town by the Northern Gate, Tseu-Hi arrived
without mishap at the Summer Palace, where she was
presently joined by most of the Princes of the Blood
and high dignitaries. There was no time to be lost,
for the foreign troops had over-run the Tartar Town
and might consequently at any moment they chose
make an immediate descent upon the Summer Palace
which was only twenty lis from Peking.

Nevertheless Tseu-Hi did not lose her head. Knowing something by past experience regarding the men-
tality of the Barbarians, she hurriedly superintended
the packing up of the principal works of art in the
various pavilions and despatched them immediately

on the road to Jehol, sending a message meanwhile to the Empress Consort, who had remained in the Forbidden City, begging her to follow her example, or at any rate to bury the imperial treasure in a safe hiding place.

Having accomplished this summary removal which she rightly regarded as indispensable, she quitted the beloved and beautiful Summer Palace, shrine of her dearest dreams, and set forth as of yore upon the road to exile. She was thus for the second time driven from her home by those same terrible Barbarians whom she loathed and cursed from the bottom of a heart that was corroded by such a succession of outrages and misfortunes.

Five Hundred Million Men

CHAPTER TWENTY-FIVE

In view of the impossibility of preparing any of the provincial functionaries for the hurried flight of the Court, the journey was accomplished in miserably uncomfortable conditions, through a country devoid of any constructed roads and where the only shelter available was to be found in ruined temples or at inns of a repulsive squalor.

None the less, since time pressed and no armed force protected the retreat from possible pursuit by the Barbarians, the imperial convoy, regardless of almost impassable earth-tracks and the most elementary means of transport, pursued their journey with the utmost celerity; a distance of some forty to fifty lis was accomplished daily, by marching from dawn until nightfall.

Having crossed the celebrated Great Wall of China and traversed the mountain passes, the exhausted fugitives finally reached Taï-Youen-Fou, the capital of Chan-Si, where they at length found decent shelter and the necessary supplies.

Hu-Yien, governor of Chan-Si, was a devoted adherent of the Manchu dynasty as well as an enthusiastic admirer of the "Boxer" movement. Fundamentally anti-foreign, he had executed to the letter the instructions that he had received from Peking, and had put to death every foreigner, man, woman or child, who could be discovered in his province.

Having devoutly performed the three genuflexions and the nine prostrations before the "old buddha" who did him the extreme honour of soliciting his protection, he conducted her in person to his Yamen, which he placed entirely at her disposal.

He proudly showed Tseu-Hi the Grand Court of Honour in which, by his order, fifty-seven Catholic and Protestant missionaries of various nationalities had been massacred. He also showed her the great sword with which, as evidence of his enthusiastic loyalty, he had personally beheaded several prisoners.

The young heir presumptive, Pou-Tsiun, irreverently seized the weapon and began to mimic the executioner's gesture. This unseasonable parody deeply shocked the Dowager Empress, who was beginning to resent the coarseness and impudence of this future Holy Man.

Already, upon more than one occasion, the son of Prince Touan, forgetful of his dignity, had allowed himself liberties that were in the worst of taste.

He had, for instance, one fine day, thought it amusing to disguise himself as a "Boxer" soldier in the courtyard of the Summer Palace, and shortly afterwards he had menaced the Holy Man with personal violence as a punishment for alleged foreign sympathies.

On both occasions Tseu-Hi had severely rebuked the imperial buffoon and had caused him to be soundly whipped by her eunuchs; but the lesson had been without effect and he remained incorrigible.

His father, Prince Touan, also displayed an odious arrogance, and Tseu-Hi both hated and despised him since the occasion on which he had led a band of "Boxers" to demand the head of the Holy Man on the threshold of her palace.

Moreover, Tseu-Hi, the ever level-headed, reflected that it was no longer opportune, now that the foreigners were victorious, to parade noisily anti-foreign and reactionary sentiments; it would have been a fatal mistake further to support the "Boxers" who had in any case shown themselves to be incapable of maintaining the struggle against the foreigners and were now no more than unruly bands of looters and rioters, which might easily become more perilous than the Barbarians themselves to the safety of the dynasty.

For these reasons, having sharply reprimanded Pou-Tsiun and Prince Touan, she was by no means lavish of her congratulations to the disconcerted governor of Chan-Si, for a zeal which she now regarded as singularly misplaced. She even gave him to understand that, should need arise, she would consider herself compelled to sacrifice him to the new policy with which she hoped to mollify the resentment of the victors.

At which juncture, Marshal Yong-Lou, having vainly sought to rally the imperial troops round Peking, abandoned a hopeless enterprise and joined the Empress at Taï-Youen-Fou.

The arrival of her loyal and courageous lover consoled Tseu-Hi who found in him an unfailing defender against the persistent intrigues of Prince Touan and the other "Boxer" chiefs who had accompanied the retreat.

She therefore received him with genuine emotion, and, under pretext of according him an audience, shut herself alone with him into one of the rooms of the Yamen. Then, for the first time, perhaps, she opened her heart to Yong-Lou, admitting the thousand moods that had preyed upon her, her disappointment, her sorrow and her humiliation at having been forced to fly before the Barbarians. She also told him of her secret hopes for the future, and of her tenacious determination to fight to the bitter end through fair weather or foul until she regained Supreme Power over the entire Celestial Empire. She concluded by telling him that she would lighten the ship, if necessary, throwing overboard both the "Boxers" and their adherents, rather than run any fatal risk.

Marshal Yong-Lou listened gravely to the Empress' revised policy, of which moreover he entirely approved, and he did his utmost to encourage her energetic resolve to keep a firm hold at any cost of the helm and to avoid total shipwreck.

In the meantime, as she seemed for the moment shattered by such a succession of emotions, he begged her to rest awhile; taking her familiarly upon his knees, he began to rock her with infinite tenderness, as though she were a little ailing child sinking at last into a restorative slumber.

And Tseu-Hi, safe from all indiscreet eyes, laid her aching head trustfully on the breast of the friend of her childhood; then she closed her eyes in order to savour a few moments of peace and forgetfulness.

The Woman Who Commanded

CHAPTER TWENTY-SIX

The die was cast; in order to save the Empire and her personal power, Tseu-Hi with disconcerting effrontery openly repudiated all those who had compromised themselves with the foreigners in the "Boxer" Rising and likewise all the nationalist and reactionary ministers whose actions and ideals she had for so long approved.

She was only too glad to get out of things so cheaply. For had she not been seriously alarmed at one time, not only for her throne but for her personal safety? It was for this reason that on her arrival at Taï-Youen-Fou, she had almost immediately thought it wise to leave for Si-Ngan, the capital of Chan-Si, having heard it rumoured that the Allies intended to despatch an army into Chan-Si to avenge the massacre of their missionaries.

How many weeks had she spent in anguish and uncertainty regarding her ultimate fate!

Fortunately she had had the good sense to recall and reappoint as governor of Petchili, the ancient Li-Houng-Tchang who, taking advantage of the semi-disgrace that had overtaken him at the time of his army's defeat by the Japanese, had remained prudently at Shanghai throughout the "Boxer" Rising.

Five Hundred Million Men

For all his eighty years, the old diplomat had remained as wily as a young fox. It was he who, together with Prince King, undertook the negotiations with the Allies, and he discharged his task so successfully, taking such advantage of the rivalries that had arisen among the powers, that he succeeded in saving not only the Empire, but the Empress Tseu-Hi into the bargain.

The conditions of the peace were indeed better than could have been hoped for. The Allies, claiming no territory, merely insisted that in order to ensure the protection of their representatives at Peking, the railway line which connected the capital with the sea should henceforth remain under international military control.

In addition, they naturally demanded an indemnity of some four hundred and fifty million taels to be annually divided between the various powers; but the absurd aspect of this clause lay in the fact that the indemnity was more than outbalanced by the raising of duty upon imports from abroad, so that the payment of the indemnity actually devolved upon the foreigners themselves.

Finally, the Allies exacted that those responsible for the "Boxer" Rising should be personally punished; and here again their views coincided with those of Tseu-Hi, by assisting her to get rid of certain important personages who obstructed her exercise of authority, and more particularly of Prince

Touan who had assumed a prominent position which was not without its anxieties for the Dowager Empress.

Since it was obviously necessary to treat with some one, the Allies adopted the fiction of settling current affairs with the phantom Son of Heaven, Kouang-Siu, thus in point of fact leaving Tseu-Hi mistress of the situation.

On learning of this stupendous diplomatic victory accomplished by old Li-Houng-Tchang, the Empress exulted, but at the same time to her hatred of the foreigners was further added a profound contempt. Having achieved victory in the field, they were proving themselves utterly incapable of profiting by their success and were lavishly displaying their foolishness and ignorance.

They left their chief adversary in possession of all her powers and appeared actually eager to smooth out any obstacles in the way of her restoration to personal authority.

It was true that they made some outward show of uniting to render her inoffensive by a common proclamation forbidding the sale of arms and ammunition, but Tseu-Hi was well aware that what was officially forbidden would in practice be winked at and that she would, as in the past, find means of obtaining the necessary armaments.

From the moment that the Dragon's Throne was once more consolidated, who was to prevent a reorganisation of the army or such preparations for a more effective mobilisation as the construction of roads and of railways? Not only was Tseu-Hi to emerge practically unscathed from the catastrophe, but she was in no way debarred from the prospect of revenge.

Fortified by this consoling reflection she waited patiently at Si-Ngan until such time as she should receive the list of political scapegoats.

Meanwhile, as evidence of her goodwill, she began by depriving Pou-Tsiun of his title as heir presumptive and published a decree abolishing all the titles and honours of his father, Prince Touan, and banishing him in perpetuity to distant Turkestan. Duke Lan, another member of the imperial family, met with the same fate, and Prince Tchouang, who had displayed such ferocity in the massacre of Christians at Peking and who had set a price on their heads, was commanded to commit suicide.

This he accomplished by very elegantly hanging himself with the traditional yellow silk bowstring which was sent him in the name of the Holy Man in an exquisite coffret of fine lacquer.

There ensued a special invitation from Tseu-Hi to many other high officials who had been involved in the "Boxer" Rising, to follow his noble example; the wives and concubines of these lords and masters duly accompanied them, as custom demanded, upon their long journey.

The Woman Who Commanded

Hu-Yien, the governor of Chan-Si, who had so enthusiastically welcomed Tseu-Hi to his Yamen, while boasting of the murder of the missionaries, was condemned to be beheaded with that same sword of execution which he had so proudly wielded.

The old minister, Kang-Hi, most violent of all anti-foreign reactionaries, had recently died during the interregnum at Si-Ngan, surrounded by every attention that the Empress could afford him; she seemed bitterly to regret the loss of so excellent a servant. He was however condemned to posthumous decapitation, which was regarded as a shameful degradation to his spirit.

Finally Tchao-Chou-Kiao, one of the most influential of Tseu-Hi's ministers, a man for whom the Empress had always expressed a genuine liking, was also informed that he must discreetly depart to a better world.

After this sensational series of executions Tseu-Hi rightly conjectured that the ire of the Barbarians would have subsided, and leaving the completion of negotiations to Li-Houng-Tchang and Prince King she resumed the reins of government with the same composure as though she had still been at Peking. She appointed a new Grand Council, issued numerous decrees and established a complicated system of etiquette in a Court which was organised at Si-Ngan exactly as it had been in the Violet Town. Marshal Yong-Lou, loaded with every conceivable honour and favour, filled the position of an all-powerful Prince Consort, while the Grand Eunuch, Li-Lien-Yn, always in high esteem, endeavoured to amuse Tseu-Hi by organising superb theatrical representations as he had done of yore at the Summer Palace.

Nevertheless, he remained somewhat anxious regarding his personal fate, for he had openly supported the "Boxers" and had preached a frenzied crusade against the foreigners. He therefore awaited with some anxiety the arrival at Si-Ngan of the list of proscriptions drawn up by the Barbarians.

But to his immense relief he was able to ascertain that it did not include his name. Out of contempt or ignorance the sea-devils had forgotten the Grand Eunuch, who was nevertheless so important a personage and who exercised so incontestable an influence in the government.

And Tseu-Hi was overjoyed at not having to sacrifice the intimate confidant who had dwelt in her shadow for so many years and who was indispensable to her for so many reasons; reasons connected not only with her exercise of imperial power, but also with the satisfaction of her feminine caprices.

CHAPTER TWENTY-SEVEN

Peace having been concluded with the Barbarians (September 7, 1901), Tseu-Hi, on the advice of Yong-Lou, decided to return to Peking and to reascend the Dragon's Throne as though nothing untoward had occurred during the preceding year.

In order to "save her face" the Empress was officially supposed to have been engaged upon a mere tour of inspection in the Western Provinces; that duty accomplished, she returned, as was right and natural, to the capital.

The journey back from Si-Ngan proved agreeable and indeed almost in the nature of a triumphal progress. Tseu-Hi voyaged by short stages, without hurrying herself the least bit in the world and selecting the best roads. She rested for several days at Ho-Nan-Fou, and then again at Kai-Foung-Fou where she celebrated with splendour her sixty-sixth birthday and received the good wishes and congratulations of her excellent subjects who still preserved their veneration for their "old buddha."

In spite of all the terrible experiences through which she had recently passed, Tseu-Hi had retained all her freshness of mind and body. She appeared

300

astoundingly young and had not lost her striking beauty.

All who beheld her were struck by the great powers of seduction that she was still able to exercise; she did not only impose herself by prestige, she enchanted those who approached her by her graciousness and charm.

She counted indeed upon these qualities to assist her in recovering the good graces of the diplomatic corps, and she worked hard to captivate the admiration and esteem of those very individuals for whose downfall she had so perfidiously schemed.

She was in fact irresistible, and she knew it!

Having for the first time in her life travelled by the railway which had been constructed with the aid of the accursed foreigners, she left the train with great ceremony and was met on the Peking platform by all the high officials of the Empire, accompanied by numerous Barbarians who bared their heads with a strange forgetfulness of their grievances.

This unexpected sight positively rejoiced Tseu-Hi; she acknowledged these foolish Barbarians with a tinge of irony, bowing to them with her clasped hands held on a level with her face; then, with great dignity she stepped into the magnificent palanquin which bore her off to the Forbidden City, there to reign again with unabated prestige.

Mute and insignificant, the wretched Holy Man followed his aunt in another palanquin. He was merely returning to his prison from which he had only been temporarily released by a sequence of unexpected events.

He was however more or less certain now of remaining alive.

Rendered wiser by experience, Tseu-Hi no longer contemplated suppressing him or even attempting to depose him. What, after all, did it matter, if the foreign ministers cherished a harmless fiction: Kouang-Siu was welcome to remain in their eyes the true Son of Heaven so long as she, dwelling in the shadow of the marionette, was free to exercise undisputed authority.

Meanwhile, immediately after her return, Tseu-Hi set to work as a good housewife to restore order in the various palaces that had been wrecked by the soldiery and to replace in the Summer Palace the works of art that she had so providentially removed.

The treasure which she had directed her niece, Long-You, to bury, at the time of the flight of the Court, she found intact, the Barbarians having failed to discover it; this fact filled her with lively satisfaction, for she appreciated money at its true value, not as one of the chief aims of life, but as a powerful weapon in the acquisition of dominion.

The Grand Eunuch, however, uttered heartrending lamentations, for the hiding place he had selected for his entire savings had been discovered by the foreign soldiery, thanks to the assistance of a disloyal servant who never again expected to set eyes on his master.

Wishing to offer some consolation to the Grand Eunuch's despair, Tseu-Hi instituted a rigorous search throughout Peking and succeeded in arresting the traitor. He was promptly beheaded, which slightly comforted Li-Lien-Yn; but he saw himself once more compelled to amass a fortune out of various shady transactions; it was a matter of beginning life all over again.

A few days later, in accordance with the prescribed conditions, Tseu-Hi officially received the foreign ministers for the solemn ratification of the Peace Treaty.

For the first time in history, Barbarians were admitted to the presence of the Son of Heaven without being constrained to perform the traditional genuflexions and prostrations. From the rather puerile standpoint of diplomatic arrogance, this was a signal victory, but Tseu-Hi regarded this trifling revenge as of small importance.

Magnificent, frozen into a hieratic attitude upon the Dragon's Throne, she received the Barbarians with incomparable dignity and endured no loss of prestige when they saluted her in the Western manner. . . . She merely considered them singularly lacking in polite education.

The Holy Man, Kouang-Siu, insignificant and torpid, occupied a wretched little throne placed well below that of the Empress, who thus emphasised the fact that she alone remained Mistress of the Celestial Empire.

Nevertheless, the diplomats saved their dignity by a pretense that they had treated exclusively with the Son of Heaven.

The following week Tseu-Hi reached the climax of impudence by inviting the "ladies" of the legations to a grand reception in the private apartments of her palace.

She displayed astounding amiability and tact, swearing by all the gods that she had endured a living death of anxiety throughout the siege of the legations, which had been instituted against her will by abominable rioters, and in a voice trembling with emotion, this amazing actress expressed the affection and admiration which she had always felt for these excellent ladies whom she would with so much secret joy have despatched to the Yellow Fountains.

She exhibited such affecting sympathy that her victims retired with an excellent impression, proud of having met the Empress on an equal footing and entirely forgetful of all the horrors that had attended the siege.

Having thus established the happiest possible relations with the foreign powers, Tseu-Hi found herself once again, but more powerfully than ever before, undisputed head of the government.

She raised to her side, as Grand Secretary and

Grand Councillor, Marshal Yong-Lou, who thus shared the glory of her apotheosis.

It must be confessed that the foreign ministers, ignorant of the real part which Yong-Lou had played during the "Boxer" crisis, viewed with an unfriendly eye the supreme elevation of this great Manchu lord who enjoyed such immense popularity among the soldiery; they received his diplomatic visit with extreme coldness. This misunderstanding of his political aims and views so saddened Yong-Lou that he begged Tseu-Hi to relieve him of his high functions.

But the Empress quickly reassured her faithful lover, pointing out that the esteem in which he might or might not be held by such uneducated persons could not be a matter of interest to anyone, and she confirmed him in his offices, assuring him as ever of her undying affection.

In the meantime Prince Tchouen, a brother of the Emperor Kouang-Siu, who bore the same name as his father, had left for Berlin with a diplomatic mission designed to present its official apologies to the Emperor William II for the murder of Baron von Ketteler. But once arrived in Germany, he refused to take part in any ceremony that he considered of a humiliating nature, and in the end William II consented, out of sheer boredom, to receiving no more than the vaguest expressions of regret from this envoy extraordinary.

The Woman Who Commanded

Prince Tchouen, on the other hand, paid careful attention to all that he saw in Germany, with a view to the reorganisation of the Chinese army and navy; he made elaborate arrangements for sending German instructors to China and for the clandestine purchase of all kinds of equipments and armaments.

In so doing, he faithfully obeyed the directions of Tseu-Hi who fully intended to profit by the lessons learnt in the school of experience and to accomplish a complete regeneration of the Celestial Empire.

Realising that China must of necessity transform herself according to the example of Japan, she had begun to elaborate a vast program of reforms, to the blank astonishment of the ancient conservatives who would never have believed the "old buddha" capable of such a volte-face.

But Tseu-Hi never hesitated to sacrifice her personal feelings to the interests of her country, and she understood that in order to defend it against the foreigners, it was necessary to adopt a friendly attitude with a view to the acquisition of their knowledge and their strength.

There again she displayed the brain power of a great statesman and showed herself infinitely superior to the hidebound old ministers by whom she was surrounded.

Five Hundred Million Men

CHAPTER TWENTY-EIGHT

In April of the year 1903, Tseu-Hi suffered a cruel blow to her dearest affections in the death of Yong-Lou, Grand Secretary and Grand Councillor to the Throne. With him disappeared an entire past of loving memories, of youth and of fiery ambitions . . . her heart was well-nigh broken.

In losing him, she lost not only the one creature whom she had truly loved, but also the securest confidant, the most devoted friend and the wisest of councillors.

She naturally gave him a most magnificent funeral, raising him by posthumous election to the highest hereditary rank and causing his Ancestral Tablet to be placed in the Temple of Great and Virtuous Mandarins. She also commanded that the story of his life should be inserted in the annals of the dynasty, thus assuring him for ever a place in History.

Then utterly inconsolable, and unable to command for him the universal mourning exclusively reserved for the sovereigns, she departed to conceal her extreme sorrow in that Summer Palace where Yong-Lou must ever survive for her as in a dream of the past.

From the moment, the woman in Tseu-Hi was dead and there remained only the Empress. More than ever, indeed, did she show herself adequate to her position. Retaining an undiminished intellectual and physical vigour, she assumed all the responsibilities and all the burdens of power, only conceding to Prince King, who had succeeded Yong-Lou as Grand Councillor, a very limited authority.

With remarkable ability, she set about preparing the union of all the provinces of her immense Empire, quieting local disputes and ancient rivalries between the North and South.

In the "Boxer" Rising, only a few Northern Provinces had suffered the foreign invasion, as indeed only the unhappy inhabitants of Petchili had paid up for the true instigators of the movement.

Now Tseu-Hi intended that in future China as a whole should be united in sentiment against the Barbarians and thus would, in case of need, rise up as one man against the tyranny.

Unfortunately, Li-Houng-Tchang had died at the close of the negotiations that he had so ably conducted. That ancient fox who so well knew the weaknesses and jealousies of the various powers and was so expert at setting them at one another's throats, was obviously a severe loss to Tseu-Hi who had found no one to replace him as a diplomatist. On the other hand, from the military standpoint Youan-Chi-Kai had been a more than worthy successor and had succeeded in reorganising at Petchili a first-class modern army.

Five Hundred Million Men

At this stage of the proceedings, Tseu-Hi was afforded the immense relief of seeing Russia and Japan engage on a long and devastating quarrel regarding the territories which they had stolen from China (1904-1905).

While the Empress deplored the fact that the struggle must take place in that Manchuria that had been the cradle of her ancestors, she welcomed each blow that fell with very evident satisfaction.

She already foresaw that the Barbarians, swollen with pride of their military forces and so inclined to confuse civilisation with mere material progress, were destined, in an appalling world war, to shed torrents of their own blood and annihilate their own prosperity. Two wild beasts were at each other's throats; the others, roused by the scent of carnage, would not be very long in following their example. In this she perceived a happy augury and the first signs of the vengeance of the Spirits of the ancient Holy Men, supported by Heaven, the protector of China.

Her confidence established in the future of her country, which need no longer fear dismemberment or division among foreign powers that were fully engaged in a life and death struggle between themselves, Tseu-Hi now gave her exclusive attention to the maintenance of order and peace in her own empire.

The Woman Who Commanded

There being no cloud to overshadow the political horizon and the Celestial Empire having recovered its ancient prosperity to which was super-added a new brilliance, Tseu-Hi resolved to consecrate the end of the year 1908 to a series of grand fêtes and official ceremonies. Her pronounced taste for the drama caused her to love all sumptuous spectacles, in which respect, as in so many others, she was entirely of her race and in communion with the Chinese spirit of theatricality. The Chinese are above all things a race of born actors and in all circumstances they adore pomp and eloquence, grandeur of gesture and an exaggeration that is tragic or comic on the slightest provocation.

The first pretext for great rejoicings was the fiftieth birthday of Youan-Chi-Kai, viceroy of Pet-chili and commander-in-chief of the army, who had little by little come to replace the deceased Yong-Lou in the heart of the Empress Dowager. He did so the more easily in that she never forgot the immense service he had rendered her in betraying to her the confidences of the unhappy Kouang-Siu.

Tseu-Hi, accompanied as always by the Grand Eunuch Li-Lien-Yn, and followed by her entire Court, assisted in person at the fêtes that constituted a triumph for Youan-Chi-Kai. The Holy Man, Kouang-Siu, chewing the cud of his impotent resentment, had remained all alone, deserted in his official prison on the Terrace of the Ocean, while Prince Touan, courageously espousing the cause of his unhappy and persecuted brother, refused to go and applaud the author of that brother's downfall.

Despite this rather discordant note, the ceremony was very resplendent and delighted the numerous spectators.

Still more rare and original a spectacle was furnished soon after by the official reception of the Dalaï-Lama who had come from distant Thibet in order to remind Tseu-Hi that although she might be the "old buddha" of politics, there existed a living Grand Buddha, only and sacred representative of Heaven on earth.

Numerous difficulties arose as to the ceremonial to be observed on this occasion, which gave immense pleasure to the experts of an incredibly complicated etiquette. They argued till they were out of breath regarding the ancient rules of conduct and upon the thorny question of temporal versus spiritual authority.

The Grand Eunuch Li-Lien-Yn, who was infinitely superstitious, whispered in every corner that the coming of a living Grand Buddha to Peking had always coincided with the death of a Son of Heaven, a ru-

The Woman Who Commanded

mour which did not fail to cast a shadow over the hearers. In point of fact, it was soon announced that Kouang-Siu had fallen dangerously ill, but it was left for conjecture to determine whether his illness was the result of the Grand Eunuch's prediction or whether that worthy had seized on the opportunity for the realisation of his dearest wish, which was the final abolition of the Holy Man. He had never forgiven the latter for having ordered his execution at the time of the unsuccessful coup d'état of 1898.

Soon afterwards, on the third of November, occurred the celebration of the Dowager Empress' seventy-third birthday, which gave rise to immense popular rejoicing in Peking, where the streets were elaborately decorated.

At the Palace itself, in the Forbidden City, preparations were made for a great theatrical performance, which was to continue for five consecutive days and nights.

Having, during the morning, received the homage and good wishes of all the state officials and a congratulatory visit from the Dalaï-Lama, Tseu-Hi, younger and more sprightly than ever, herself opened the fête, dressed as the Goddess of Mercy and surrounded by eunuchs, concubines and the imperial princesses also disguised as legendary characters.

A grand banquet then took place in the open air on the shores of the lake opposite the Pavilion of the Terrace of the Ocean, where the Holy Man, Kouang-

Siu, lay dying. This fact in no wise affected Tseu-Hi who did honour to the repast and was in the best of humours.

But as the season was already advanced and the evenings were becoming frosty, the Empress caught a chill at nightfall, which was further complicated by the fact that, contrary to her habit, she had slightly overindulged her appetite for sour milk and green apples, of which she was inordinately fond. During the night she had a further attack of the dysentery which had troubled her three months earlier at the Summer Palace during the hot weather. The attack was a particularly severe one and it left Tseu-Hi completely exhausted.

Nevertheless, she set herself with superhuman determination to combat her physical weakness, while entertaining no illusions as to her imminent demise.

Learning of her grave condition the Dalaï-Lama sent her a miraculous image of Buddha designed to protect her against the adverse influence of certain stars.

Tseu-Hi, somewhat reassured, sent Prince King to deposit the image upon the altar of the mausoleum which she had had erected for herself at a distance of some three hundred lis to the east of Peking. She then addressed herself as courageously to affairs of State as though she had been in excellent health.

But the dysentery persisted and Tseu-Hi's strength declined day by day.

The Woman Who Commanded

On the other hand, a distressing coincidence occurred in the official announcement that the Holy Man, Kouang-Siu, was nearing his end, being naturally unable to commit the unseemliness of surviving his venerable aunt.

On the thirteenth of November, Prince King, having safely performed his mission of depositing the miraculous image of Buddha at the mausoleum, returned in all haste, summoned by the Empress who informed him that Kouang-Siu, about to die, desired to nominate his successor.

Grand Audience was at once convened in the Hall of the Phoenix, at which Tseu-Hi contrived to preside, despite her fast failing strength.

Half dying, she still had the amazing energy to oppose victoriously Prince Ping and Youan-Chi-Kai who wished to nominate Prince Pou-Louen or Prince Kuong, nephew of the former celebrated prince of that name and last of the great-grandsons of the Emperor Tao-Kouang. Achieving her final coup d'état, Tseu-Hi elected as future Son of Heaven the young Pou-Yi who was only three years of age, but who was the son of Yong-Lou's daughter whom Tseu-Hi had married to Prince Tchouen in order to honour and reward the friend of her childhood. As for Prince Tchouen himself, he was appointed to be Regent at the death of his brother, Kouang-Siu.

In spite of his devotion to Tseu-Hi, Youan-Chi-Kai attempted to protest, for Prince Tchouen had prom-

314

ised his brother eventual vengeance for the betrayal
of 1908.

But Tseu-Hi silenced him with the assurance that
she was not yet dead and would as in the past know
how to control the situation. She simply conceded,
in deference to custom, that Pou-Yi should be proclaimed adopted heir to the Emperor Toung-Tche,
who, since the accession of Kouang-Siu, had remained
without any direct descendant to offer him ancestral
worship. But she also decreed, against all precedent,
that Pou-Yi should likewise be regarded as adopted
heir to Kouang-Siu. This placed the child in the
position of being not only the son of his natural
father, Prince Tchouen, but also of two posthumous
fathers, Toung-Tche and Kouang-Siu. This constituted a terrific revolution in the domain of tradition,
but no one dared so much as to breathe a protest.

The decree was therefore immediately drawn up
and countersigned establishing Pou-Yi as future Holy
Man, to reign under the name of Sieng-Toung. The
imperial baby was promptly sent for and presented
to his great-aunt as also to his dying predecessor,
Kouang-Siu.

Tseu-Hi actually found the strength to attend this
latter ceremony at the Terrace of the Ocean, and she
remained there, in the company of Long-You, who
had so well guarded her husband, in order to attend
the last moments of the Holy Man.

To the very end, Kouang-Siu displayed the more

regrettable aspects of his character, utterly refusing to assume the ritual robe of longevity in which tradition demands that a Holy Man should die.

Having ascertained that he was at last really dead, Tseu-Hi returned to her palace in order to concoct an official testament supposed to be that of the deceased Emperor and confirming all the Empress' dispositions. On that evening Tseu-Hi almost appeared to have conquered her illness, thanks to her vitality and her robust constitution.

The next morning at six o'clock she was again at work. She began by having a lengthy interview with the new Regent, Prince Tchouen, father of Pou-Yi, the infant Holy Man, giving him to understand that his authority would be strictly limited and that she would herself continue to hold the reins of government. She then spent an affectionate hour with the wife of Prince Tchouen, who was the daughter of Yong-Lou, recalling at great length the admirable qualities of her beloved friend.

Finally she had a last secret interview with Long-You, her favourite niece, the easily consolable widow of the miserable Kouang-Siu.

It was decided that Long-You should in her turn assume the title of Empress Dowager, while Tseu-Hi would be known as the Grand Empress Dowager.

During the entire morning, Tseu-Hi worked furiously, regulating with her usual precision the smallest details with regard to the titles and duties of every member of the New Government. Towards the Hour of the Sheep she sat down at the table as usual and ate with considerable appetite; but she had overdone things during the past few days and she was suddenly seized again with an attack of dysentery so violent that she lost consciousness.

When she came to her senses she realised that this time the moment was at hand for her departure on the long journey.

Collecting her failing forces, she still had the energy and the presence of mind to summon in haste to her palace the Regent and Long-You, the new Empress Dowager, as well as all the members of the Grand Council; in their presence she dictated her last decree in which she confirmed all her decisions of the previous day with regard to the exercise of power during Pou-Yi's minority. She insisted upon the capital point that no important action could be taken by the Regent without the consent of the Empress Dowager Long-You, whom she thus elected as her personal successor, supposing her always to be adequate to the task.

After the promulgation of this final decree, Tseu-Hi drew up her personal testament which contained, as was customary, a brief survey of her policy with the necessary indications to insure its continuation.

Finally, having assumed the ritual funeral robes and extended herself ceremoniously upon a state bed, she awaited death with courage and dignity, retaining in spite of her sufferings an impassive countenance and continuing to express herself with entire lucidity and extreme elegance.

And yet, a few moments before her death, she seemed to receive a terrible shock. Suddenly she had realised the grim fact that no one would be able to replace her; that since the entire political and social edifice rested solely upon her shoulders, it would inevitably crumble after her death.

Like all great autocrats and like all the founders of vast empires, Tseu-Hi had committed only one error, but that one was of capital importance, for it was that of concentrating in her own person all the strength, all the initiative and all the organisation of the State; it followed necessarily that her achievement, great as it had been, could not survive her.

With extreme anguish, she began to deplore her imminent dissolution, which would be the signal for the débâcle, and she clung desperately to life.

But her breath was already failing . . . and her attendants approached her respectfully, begging her to conform to custom and to pronounce her valedictory words.

Then the beholders witnessed a terrible occurrence: Her features became convulsed and she forced herself to an utterance that seemed to give the lie to her whole existence.

"Never again allow a woman to assume the supreme power, or eunuchs to meddle with affairs of

State . . . at the head of the Celestial Empire, a man is required . . . yes, indeed, a strong man! . . ."

And with these words she died, her mouth remaining wide open, which, according to common belief in the Far East, signifies that the soul has been unwilling to leave the body. . . . Those who were present, however, remarked with satisfaction that the Divine Empress had to the end retained sufficient self-possession to turn her face to the South in conformity with age-old Ritual.

THE END